C000246798

THE ELUSIVE OBVIOUS

PREFACE

To The Reader

The Elusive Obvious deals with simple, fundamental notions of our daily life that through habit become elusive. "Time is money" is obviously a good attitude to have in business or work. It is not at all obvious that in love the same attitude is the cause of so much unhappiness. We often make mistakes. We carry over from one activity to another attitudes of mind that do not make life what it could be.

Romance is obviously a fine thing. Romantic love is enchanting, but not so good if one partner is money-minded and the other is romantic. In time, they will finish at the psychiatrist's or in court.

Many troubled relationships come from inadvertently carrying over seemingly good habits of thought to where they do not apply. Somehow we behave as if good habits are always good. We think or rather feel that we need not bother about behaving otherwise. It is not so obvious that good habits can make us unhappy. It is an elusive truth. Yet habitual lack of free choice is often, nay, usually, disastrous.

If you come across something obviously new to you, in its form at least, please stop for a moment and look inward. Working out new alternatives assists us to grow stronger and wiser. My editor tells me that I should free readers from having to think and look inward. I believe she knows what the average reader likes. I myself do not like predigested food. For you, the reader, I have added to the beginning and end of each chapter a short introduction and summary to facilitate your digestion so that you will find it easier to make what is elusive more obvious.

THE ELUSIVE OBVIOUS
or
BASIC FELDENKRAIS

Publications by Dr. FELDENKRAIS

JUDO – Frederick Warne, London 1941 (8 editions).

BODY AND MATURE BEHAVIOUR Routledge and Kegan Paul, London 1949, International Universities Press, New York 1950. International Universities Press, Paperback 1970. Alef Publishers, Tel Aviv 1966.

HIGHER JUDO (Ground work) Fredrick Warne, London 1952 (3 editions)

AWARENESS THROUGH MOVEMENT, Harper and Row, New York 1972.

TWENTY-FIVE LESSONS by Dr. Moshe Feldenkrais. Noa Eshkol, Faculty of Fine Arts, Tel-Aviv University, 1977. The Movement Notation Society Israel, 2nd improved edition.

ADVENTURES IN THE JUNGLE OF THE BRAIN, THE CASE of NORA, Harper and Row Publishers, 1977, Alef Publishers Tel Aviv, 1978, in Hebrew, German, and French.

Meta Publications, P.O. Box 1910, Capitola, CA 95010
PH: (831) 464-0254   FAX: (831) 464-0517
www.meta-publications.com

ISBN 10: 0-916990-09-5
ISBN 13: 978-0-916990-09-1
Library of Congress Catalog Card Number: 81-82159

© 1981 by M. Feldenkrais. All rights reserved.
Published 1981
This book or parts thereof may not be
reproduced in any form without written
permission of the publisher.
Printed in the United States of America.

CONTENTS

I would like to thank the architect, Allison Downs. Without her sharp critical understanding this book and "The Case of Nora" would not be what they are. Besides that, she did all the typing. Only a lifelong friend could do that for me.

FOREWORD

Are you satisfied with your posture? Are you satisfied with your breathing? Are you satisfied with your life? I mean, do you feel you have made the best you could of your genetic endowment? Have you learned to do what you wish to do with yourself and how to do it? Do you suffer chronic pains? Do you regret not being able to do the things you would have liked to do? I believe what you wish secretly is not in fact wishful thinking, but that we are all able to live the way we want. The main obstacle is ignorance: scientific ignorance, personal ignorance, and cultural ignorance. If we do not know what we are actually enacting then we cannot possibly do what we want. I spent nearly forty years first learning to know how I was doing what, and then teaching others to learn to learn so that they could do justice to themselves. I believe that knowing oneself is the most important thing a human being can do for himself. How can one know oneself? By learning to act not as one should, but as one does. We have great difficulty in sorting out what we do as we should from what we want to do with ourselves.

The majority of people in each generation stop growing with sexual maturity, when they are considered to be adult and feel themselves adult. Most learning achieved after that involves essentially what is important socially, and personal evolution and growth are mostly accidental or a fluke. We learn a profession most of the time by opportunity rather than by continu-

ous genetic development and growth. Only artistically inclined people, be they cobblers, musicians, painters, sculptors,
actors, dancers, and some scientists continue to grow personally as well as professionally and socially. Others grow mostly
socially and professionally and remain adolescent or infantile
emotionally and sensorially and consequently also arrested in
their motor functions. Their posture grows worse, and movements or actions are gradually excluded from their repertory.
First jumping, then turning a somersault, then twisting, in
whatever order, are so eliminated or neglected that in a short
time it is impossible for them to perform these actions any
more.

People in the arts do, by dint of the art, continue to improve,
differentiate, and vary their motor skills until old age. They
continue to grow, gradually achieving a performance fitting
their intention. Obviously, there are artists in all walks of life,
but regrettably few among the rank and file.

Reading this book may help you to a happier road more in
the direction of your individuality than the high road you are
usually set upon. There is no intention to correct you. Your
trouble and mine is that we are trying to behave correctly, as
one should, at the cost of quenching, with our own consent, our
individuality. In the end we do not know what we want, to the
point of believing that what we are doing is what we really
want to do; moreover the annoying status quo becomes more
attractive to us than what we believe or say that we want. An
obvious solution is to preoccupy ourselves not with what we do
but how we do it. The "how" is the hallmark of our individuality; it is an inquiry into the process of acting. If we look at how
we do things, we might find an alternative way of doing them,
i.e. have some free choice. For, if we have no alternative, we
have no choice at all. We may kid ourselves that we have
chosen a unique way of doing things, but it is compulsive for
lack of alternatives.

It is not easy to see how you can be assisted in your task by a book, or by anything else. The thinking is exhilarating, but the communication of the thinking through words is a stumbling block. Speaking is not thinking, although sometimes it is. Anyhow, let us have a go at it. I enjoy your company and hope you will come to enjoy mine.

This is the fourth of my books on this subject in English. It was written at Peter Mayer's request and in response to my students' demand for a work condensing the four years' teaching given during summer vacations that led to their graduation and the formation of the Feldenkrais Guild in San Francisco. Most of the content of this book is not to be found in my former publications. The material is new; it is the writer who is older.

49 Nachmani St.
Tel-Aviv.

INTRODUCTION

I am known for the beneficial effects of what I call "Functional Integration" and "Awareness through Movement." In both these techniques I use everything I have learned to improve the health, mood, and ability to overcome difficulties, pain, and anxiety of the people who turn to me for help.

In my twenties, while playing left back in soccer, I badly injured my left knee and could not walk properly for several months. In those days knee surgery was not the simple intervention that it is today. It was learning to function with a knee like mine which impressed upon me the urgency of doing something more. Our knowledge will undoubtedly improve in the future, but with good theory much of what we know now can be useful and applicable.

I have tried to write only what is necessary for you to understand *how* my techniques work. I have deliberately avoided answering the *whys*. I know how to live and how to use electricity, but I encounter enormous difficulties if I attempt to answer why I live and why there is electricity. In interpersonal affairs *why* and *how* are not so sharply divided and are used indiscriminately. In science, we really only know how.

I was born in the small Russian town of Baranovitz, and at the time of the Balfour Declaration, when I was fourteen, I went all by myself to the British mandatory territory of Palestine. There I worked for several years as a pioneer, largely in a manual capacity. At the age of twenty-three I matriculated;

1

I had studied mathematics and then served for five years in the Surveying Department doing the mathematics for producing maps. I saved sufficient money to travel to Paris where I took an engineering degree in mechanics and electricity, and proceeded to the Sorbonne to read for a doctorate. While at the Sorbonne I was attached to the laboratory of Joliot-Curie who later, of course, received the Nobel Prize. At the same time I met Professor Kano, the creator of Judo, and with help from him and his pupils Yotazo Sigimura (6th Dan) the Japanese ambassador, and Kawaishi I gained my Judo Black Belt. I formed the first Judo Club in France, which today has nearly a million members. After the German invasion of France in the Second World War I escaped to England, and worked there as a scientific officer in the antisubmarine establishment of Scientific and Technical Pools of the British Admiralty until the end of the war. I participated in the Budokwai in London before finally returning to Israel to be the first director of the Electronic Department of the Defense Forces of Israel.

At the age of fifty or so, after writing *Body and Mature Behaviour,* first published in England in 1949 by Routledge and Kegan Paul, I encountered many people who thought I had some extraordinary knowledge which could perhaps help them. That book was an exposition of the up-to-date scientific knowledge of the time which had led me to my practical applications. My views on anxiety and falling, and the importance of the vestibular branch of the eighth cranial nerve are now almost universally accepted. As a result of the needs of others, I gradually developed Functional Integration and Awareness through Movement which I have subsequently taught in a dozen or so countries of the world. During this process of helping and teaching I have been privileged to examine, by touching and moving, more human heads than I dare to say. They have come from all walks of life and from many races, cultures, religions, and all ages. The youngest was a five-week-old baby whose neck was injured at birth by forceps, and the oldest was a ninety-seven year old Canadian who had been electrocuted and was paralyzed for over thirty years.

I have also handled many workers from a very wide range of activities. These details are of little importance other than to demonstrate that the primary and real object of my learning is the practical effectiveness of my actions. I am still learning, reading, and annotating several books a month in spite of my multiple obligations and travels. Some of the authors I would like you also to read; many of them are priceless: Jacques Monod, Schrödinger, J. Z. Young, Konrad Lorentz, Milton Erickson. They all discuss philosophy, semantics, and evolution, and they show an insight and knowledge of the psychophysical world which is edifying as well as interesting.

I touch with my hands and this I have done to many thousands, be they white, mongolian, black, or of whatever human species exist. This touching, handling, manipulating of living human bodies enables me to see in the books of these superb writers and turn into practice the science they teach. Probably they themselves do not know, how useful their knowledge is already when translated into the nonverbal language of the hands, i.e. Functional Integration, and the verbal Awareness through Movement.

I suggest, and I believe that I am right, that sensory stimuli are closer to our unconscious, subconscious, or autonomous functioning than to any of our conscious understanding. On the sensory level communication is more direct with the unconscious, and is therefore more effective and less distorted than at the verbal level. Words, as somebody said, are more to hide our intentions than to express them. But, I have never met anybody, man or animal, who cannot tell a friendly touch from an evil one. Touching, if unfriendly even in thought, will make the touched stiff, anxious, expecting the worst, and therefore unreceptive to your touch. Through touch, two persons, the toucher and the touched, can become a new ensemble: two bodies when connected by two arms and hands are a new entity. These hands sense at the same time as they direct. Both the touched and the toucher feel what they sense through the connecting hands, even if they do not understand and do not know what is being done. The touched person becomes aware of what the touching person feels and, without understanding, alters his configuration to conform to what he senses is wanted from him. When touching I seek nothing from the person I touch; I only feel what the touched person needs, whether he knows it or not, and what I can do at that moment to make the person feel better.

It is essential to understand what I mean by "better" and "more human." These apparently simple words do not mean the same thing to all of us. The things a handicapped person cannot do have a different meaning to him than to a healthy person. I remember a boy of thirteen brought to me by his mother. He came into the world with his right arm first, and not his head as is customary. He had no luck, and an inexperienced doctor, or whoever it was, pulled him out by his protruding arm. The right clavicle was broken, which is not a serious matter at that age, but a brachial plexus was damaged. The arm became flaccid, hanging helplessly, in spite of the fact that his mother had taken him to see every specialist who might have been able to help. I may tell you later how he learned to drive a car, became a father of healthy children, and a professor of mechanics.

When the boy became one with me he told me, with tears running down his cheeks, something you will never guess— anyway, I was surprised: he complained nobody had ever hit him at school, in spite of all his provocations. Whatever he did his schoolmates would not touch him, as teachers and parents had all impressed upon them that he was not to be hurt. He was miserable because he had never had the pleasure of being beaten up. Think, now, what "better" and "more human" meant to this boy. His mother did not know what was needed, and neither did anybody else. When I touched him he felt as one with me, and he sensed that I knew he was miserable and that I had no pity. At that point he could tell me what it was impossible for him to utter to anyone else. It was a nonverbal situation as I had asked nothing. What happened that enabled him to cry and then talk to me?

A girl with cerebral palsy, aged fifteen, was brought to me from Paris. Her mother was the principal of a lycée and could not leave, so her father brought her, and her grandmother stayed with her in Tel-Aviv. She also surprised me, for she wanted to be a dancer; this when she had never been able to put her heels on the floor and could not bend her knees, which knocked into each other at every step. If you have ever seen a person severely affected with cerebral palsy you may be able to imagine her arms, spine and gait. Nobody with common sense could think that she was so unaware of her condition as to have such an idea about herself. My job, nothing more or less, was to help her to be what she wanted, and she did, several years later, join a dancing class in Paris. I would like you to think about what was "better" and "more human" for this girl. She was a bright girl at the top of her class right up until the time she went to the university, and I promise myself to look her up next time I am in Paris.

I hope you will not jump to the conclusion that I am concerned only with cripples. To me they are all just people who seek help to be better and more human. Many doctors, actors, orchestral conductors, athletes, engineers, psychiatrists, architects, housewives—the whole range of what we can be—all sense that it would be better to be better and more human one way or another.

In fact, if normal intelligent people had more wisdom, I would give them all my attention. Their growth would make a difference to life in general. When I first began to work with people as such it was with Professor J. D. Bernal, a man of almost universal culture; Lord Boyd-Orr, Professor of Medicine and first President of the World Health Organization;

Professor Aaron Katzir, Director of the Weitzman Institute; and David Ben-Gourion, founder of the State of Israel—all of them extraordinary human beings, famous, successful, and socially integrated. J. G. Crowther who was then the Secretary of the British Council, on hearing Bernal praise my work exclaimed, "There are probably only another three brains like his so you will not reach many more." As it turns out, socially successful, very clever, important, creative people may devote no time to their personal growth. They find their whole life is their work, ignoring themselves far too often. Such people listen to me seriously only when they are incapacitated one way or another. Even so, I have reached by now thousands of them through their misfortunes. It is sad to admit that it was only by attending to the crippled that I was able to learn how to help normal people as well. This is a generalization which, fortunately, was not always true.

I believe that it is as important for me to share some of my thoughts and experiences with you as it is for you to understand them. This is because they may assist you to improve your life experience, as they helped me. You may learn to make your life more as you wish it to be; your dreams could become more precise and, who knows, they may even come true.

While writing, I am aware of only some parts of my body and also of some of my activity. You, while reading, are equally aware of only some parts of yourself and of parts of your activity. Immense activity goes on in both of us, far greater than we appreciate or are aware of. This activity is related to what we have *learned* during our whole life from inception to this moment. Our actions largely depend on our heredity, on what we have been through in our lives, on the image we have formed of ourselves, on the physical, cultural, and social environments in which we have grown and the ones in which we now function. The activity in us which makes me write and you read is mostly autonomous, some of which can be said to be unconscious and some intentional. While writing, my conscious intentional activity seems to be the only one that concerns me. I have only occasionally to pay attention to my spelling or the flow of words. I feel that I am fitting words to my thoughts. Words have slightly different meanings, and I wish to be very clear. Yet I am not sure that I choose fitting words for you; that what you understand by the words "autonomous," "unconscious," or "conscious" is what I intend to convey to you.

For many years I have been involved in working with people who have turned to me for help. Some complain of physical pain, others of mental anguish, and only a few ever speak of emotional troubles. I have some difficulty in explaining to my followers that I am not a therapist and that my touching a person with my hands has no therapeutic or healing value, though people improve through it. I think that what happens to them is *learning,* but few agree with this. What I am doing does not resemble teaching as understood at present. The accent is on the learning process, rather than on the teaching technique. After each session my pupils have a new sense of well-being: they feel taller, lighter, and breathe more freely. They often rub their eyes as if they have just woken from a sound and refreshing sleep. More often than not they say that they have become relaxed. The pain is always abated and often it is gone altogether. In addition, face wrinkles nearly always disappear, the eyes become brighter and larger, and the voice deeper and more resonant. The pupil becomes youthful again.

How can such changes in mood and attitude be brought about by just touching, however cleverly, another person's body? My pupils try to convince me that I possess the healing touch. I have taught students to do what I do in Israel, the United States, and elsewhere, so that they all now have "healing hands." They were not specially chosen, but they were selected for their academic education and their wish and capacity to learn. At the beginning, in order to explain to my students what happens between me and my clients—I say "clients" reluctantly in order not to confuse you, although they are in fact pupils but not students—I tell them this story. Imagine a dancing party attended by a man who never dances, for reasons best known to himself. He always declines all invitations to participate saying that he does not know how. One woman, however, likes the man sufficiently to persuade him to take the floor. Moving herself, she somehow manages to make him move too. The dance is not very complicated, and after a few awkward moments when his ear tells him that the music has something to do with it, he becomes conscious that her movements are rhythmical. Nevertheless, he is relieved when the dance stops and he can return to his seat and breathe again. At the end of the evening he finds he can follow her movements and steps more easily, and can even avoid bumping into her feet. Half thinking, he feels that perhaps he has not performed so badly, although he knows that he still cannot dance.

After going to a second party, he makes sufficient progress to shake his conviction that dancing is not for him. At the next party, finding a woman left sitting alone like himself, he asks her to dance, still protesting that he is not very good. Ever since then he has danced, forgetting to begin with an apology.

Consider the woman who could dance, and how she made a pupil or client dance also, without teaching musical rhythms, dancing steps, and all the rest of it. Her friendly attitude and her experience made him learn without any formal teaching. A certain kind of knowledge can pass from one person to another without a healing touch. However, the man must have learned to use his legs, hands, and the rest of him before a friendly touch could help him to use his experience and learn to dance so easily. He learned notwithstanding his ignorance of his latent ability.

In saying that I work with people I mean that I am "dancing" with them. I bring about a state in which they learn to do something without my teaching them, any more than the woman taught the dancer. We shall see later in a more detailed fashion that, in general, we do much without knowing consciously how we do it. We speak and we do not know how we do it. We swallow and ignore how we do it. Try to explain to a Martian how we swallow and you will realize what I mean by knowing. Some very common everyday acts, like sitting or getting up from a chair, seem easier to know. But, are you really sure of what we do when getting up from the sitting position? Which part of our body initiates the movement? Is it the pelvis, the legs, or the head? Do we contract our abdominal muscles first or the extensors of the back? We can do the movement just by intending to perform it and not knowing how we do it. Do you think that we really do not need to know? Suppose that somebody cannot get up for some reason, (and there are more reasons for that than meet the eye), and asks you for help. You can show him that you can get up, but then he knew that. So it seems you can do it but cannot explain how you do it. Suppose you are in need of the explanation, for how can we be sure that without knowing how we do something it is being done as well as our potential capacity will allow? Certainly most of the simple actions we do are good enough to meet our needs. Even so, every one of us feels that some actions are not as good as we would wish them to be. We organize our life around that which we can do to our satisfaction, and avoid those acts where we feel we are inept. We decide that the activities that involve our ineptitudes are not congenial to our character, are uninteresting, and we usually have more important things to do.

I did not draw in my early life for there were no drawing lessons in the schools in those good old days. One had, instead, to prepare for an active and socially useful life. When my book *Body and Mature Behaviour* was published after the Second World War I did not realize that I had changed my future in the direction it was to take me. One morning a medical doctor in London telephoned me, said he had read my book, and asked when I had studied with Heinrich Jacoby. He had recognized in my book some of the things he had received from this great teacher. He had difficulty in believing that it was the first time I had heard that name mentioned. To come to the point, he suggested that he should arrange for me to meet Heinrich Jacoby for our mutual benefit. Heinrich Jacoby lived at that time in Zurich and was much senior to me, not only in age; I felt this very clearly when I learned that what I had believed to be my personal discovery was in a way the kind of thing he had been teaching for years to a distinguished group of disciples comprising scientists, doctors, artists, and the like.

A few months later, when I could avail myself of my annual leave from the laboratory where I worked at the time as a research physicist, I went to meet Jacoby at the date he had fixed for me. I would very much like to tell you what happened during the three weeks I stayed with him and of all our conversations and mutual teaching, which often meant we saw the sun rise before we went to sleep. A book would be rather long if I were to relate all the important things I learned and those he said he learned from me. I will, however, tell you of my first overwhelming experience in drawing which I had with him, as it concerns the kind of learning we are dealing with.

I was an athlete of some repute and of strong build. Jacoby was a tiny, fragile little man who had learned to walk, he told me, when he was seven years old. He looked like, and was a hunchback, but moved gracefully. Even so, my first impression was that the man was no match for me. I felt that way in the back of my consciousness although I was certain that I had done the right thing to visit him. After a few minutes, when he explained that I was being recorded on tape and photographed by his cinecamera, he offered me a sheet of drawing paper, charcoal, and a piece of soft bread to be used as an eraser. He then asked me to draw as best I could the lamp on the piano in front of me. I told him that I had never drawn anything before except for the technical drawings I had to do for my engineering degree before reading physics at the Sorbonne, which brought me later to the Joliot-Curie Laboratory, my doctorate, and all the rest. He replied that he knew all that but I should nevertheless have a try as he had something else in mind other than just to see me draw. I drew a vertical cylinder with a truncated cone at the upper end and a kind of ellipse at the bottom for a stand. It looked to me to be a lampstand as good as I thought a lampstand drawn by me could be. He looked at the drawing and said it was the thought of a lamp and not the lamp, and I realized then that I had drawn the abstract notion of the word "lamp." All the same, I retorted, only a painter could do what he expected of me, and I was no painter as I had said before I started.

He insisted that I should try again and draw only what I saw and not what I thought I saw. I just did not know how one draws what one sees. In my, and may be also your, way of thinking he asked me to be a painter when I was not a painter. "Tell me what do you see?" "A lamp," I said. "Do you see any of the outlines which you have drawn?" I had to admit that I could not identify in my drawing a single line of the real lamp, except that the proportions were more or less those of the lamp in front of me. "Do you see lines?" Again I had to admit that none of the lines on my drawing were actually to be seen. "If you do not see lines, then what do you see when looking at this lamp? What do your eyes see in general? They see light, then why do you not draw the lighter and darker patches which you see. You have charcoal in your hand, and if you put too much of it on the paper then you have the bread to remove the superfluous and obtain some grading of the patches so that they become more as you see them."

I took another sheet of paper and this time started with dark patches of charcoal where there was no light, then it dawned on me that nowhere were there brighter patches than where

I put no charcoal on the paper. The stand was no cylinder, the shade on the top was no truncated cone, and the bottom was no ellipse. I had extraordinary feelings when I looked at the assembly of charcoal rubbings and the parts removed with the bread kneaded with my fingers. This drawing was not mine, but one which I thought only a painter could do. I had not even tried to think that way before because it had felt to me to be like cheating, pretending to be what I was not.

I believe you are understanding for yourself the extraordinary transformation that was occurring in me. I am not a painter, but then who is? When I do or act painter, the result is what only a painter can do. Am I being changed, am I losing my identity? I did not really think in those terms at that moment, but I felt unsafe because of the change which operated in me under Jacoby's questioning. He did not show me how to do it. Remember the dancer with his girlfriend? Can you see anything in common in the two cases of learning in two such different circumstances? I can.

When I left Jacoby and went to my room I saw there on the table a glass jug half filled with water. I felt an inner challenge —no, an inner conviction—which expressed itself in an urge to reproduce the jug on paper. Childishly, I also thought that I could show Jacoby that I was not really so inept as I appeared to him. I did not draw any lines at all but used instead minor touches, and the rest was blobs of light and dark. When it was finished you could see the level of water, the play of light in the water as distinct from the light on the glass, although both were transparent. I felt that I had produced a masterpiece and I believed that I had grown taller by six inches at least.

It turned out that there is no limit to the quality of being a painter, and I have to make an effort not to tell you how I became a real painter during the few weeks when I danced with Jacoby, who never taught or showed me how to paint or draw. With his tongue in his cheek he asked me why I did not follow my own teaching when I drew.

THE ORGANISM

Some universal factors influence the existence of life. They had something to do with the first living cell formed about two billion years ago. The first living cell needed shelter from radiation which formed it, and killed it as easily. Form, surface tension, surface to volume ratio, gravitation, internal processes, external changes and effects are as active today as they always were. The boundary of a living cell and any being still mediates between internal and external life, as at their origin. Here we discuss some of the factors involved.

An assembly of cells is not a tissue any more than an assembly of neurons is a brain. Bricks are not a building. All the entries in a dictionary are but words, a smaller number of which may be a sentence. Something happens to a number of identical particles or units acting together which is of a higher level, in the sense that a new quality appertains which does not exist in any one of the units separately. This higher level is reached when the units are involved in a common activity or undergo the same stress. An assembly of cells may become a liver; bricks functioning together as a load-bearing structure may become a building. Cells are linked in groups to form organs which are similar in all mammals. Organs in turn are grouped to form organisms which are of a higher level than organs. Bacteria, algae, and all other living entities have three activities in common: (1) self-reproduction, (2) self-maintenance, and (3) self-preservation. Self-reproduction is by far the least critical in time, whereas breathing, drinking, and eating limit life with greater stringency, and the lack of self-preservation may mean loss of life within less than a second. These three phenomena can be observed in both vegetation and animals, the difference being that vegetative life is passive in dealing with them. Without the effect of wind, rain, insects, animal furs and a host of other carriers and active elements, vegetation would cease to reproduce and would disappear from the earth. On the other hand, animals of all kinds are active in sustaining the three essential requirements by (4) self-propulsion, which is also self-direction, thus making movement the most important clue to animal life.

The first piece of matter having an enclosing membrane separating it from the rest of the world had form or shape and became the first individuum. The cosmos containing the membrane ensured the intake of further matter to provide the energy for self-propulsion and the discharge to the outside world of matter emptied of energy as well as the removal of the poisons of metabolism and dead particles. Every living thing has a boundary separating it from the rest of the world. The content within the boundary has structure which functions to assure the self-propulsion, i.e. the activity, of the being. When function ceases, only form and structure remain: the being is then dead. Cessation of movement is the end of life itself.

Not only is life complex to begin with, it tends to evolve towards even greater complexity, an attribute that seems vital for life to persist. Each species of animal has its own method of self-propulsion necessary for the maintenance of the other three features essential for perpetuating life. Therein lies the complexity. The structures and the functions are interdependent and both are intimately related to the environment. Without light of the appropriate wavelengths there would be no eyes and no seeing; and there are electromagnetic vibrations of waves above and below those that make up the spectrum of human vision. Moreover, light changes in intensity and objects are small and large, near and far away. These factors together with the ability to distinguish colors of great variety and subtlety only begin to illustrate the complexity of the formation of vision, as well as the form of the eyes.

All animals have an embryonic life before they are separated physically from the witness who is always there to usher them into the outside world. During embryonic life there is growth of the structures functioning in a rudimentary way in an environment that is simpler and less varying than the outside world. It is obvious that only some form of orderly development will turn two cells into a mammal, let alone a man. "Controls" is the word that comes most readily to mind: controls that assure this orderly development of the structures, their form, and the gradual bettering of their functioning. With the increasing complexity of the species, a special structure, formed to assure the necessary controls of the organism. The nervous tissues with their synapses, dendrites and relays of all kinds, function for this purpose. (Is it "purpose"?).

Control in biology as well as in cybernetics is necessary only if there is a preferred mode of function. In animals it is the optimum that is the preferred state or mode. Any deviation from the optimum is corrected. As there are literally thousands of deviations on all levels—cellular, circulatory, structural and functional—there is also a hierarchial organization of the controls.

Control and hierarchy must be stripped of the emotion attached to them in normal speaking. If the organism slips on a banana skin the highest control in the brain dealing with intentional action and movement is too slow to prevent falling. It will switch itself off to allow some older part to take over. Parts that are more primitive and evolutionarily older are faster and have shorter communication lines. There is nothing in controls and hierarchy but orderly cooperation for assuring the optimal existence of the individual.

Growth in the hierarchy, the controls, and the nervous tissues organizing them, as well as in the entire organism—its bones, muscles, and internal organs—involves reacting to the environment, adjusting to it in order to manipulate it. To achieve optimal function while growing there must be continuous change in the direction of improvement. Such a complex process will be dealing with errors and will continue without any clear purpose to achieve. It is a process of learning which is quite different from the formal academic education in schools: it is concerned essentially with "how" rather than "what" we do. A detailed inquiry into these matters is fundamental and essential.

Again, the complexity of this process is so great that failure to achieve is inherent. In ordinary conditions it is very rare to find the optimum in structure, form, and function. Dysfunction in movement, regressions, and partial development are to be expected. This generality makes it possible to help normal individuals achieve the optimal development which they would otherwise fail to do.

A nervous system consisting of an astronomical number of cells ($3 \cdot 10^{10}$) is fit to live and function in a great variety of physical worlds. Even a nervous system like ours stands up to lack of gravitation, to lack of visual and auditory stimulation, as the experience of so many astronauts has shown. It is enough to initiate any activity in which the cues occur at sufficiently close intervals for the system to work. I believe that our nervous system would function well in a thousand different possible worlds. It would grow and adapt itself and act in any conditions in which life can exist. Our nervous system is in fact "wired in" to cope with equal ease with any one of the few thousand languages and dialects that exist on earth.

We are so familiar with ourselves that we fail to appreciate what we have said. What do we mean by a nervous system functioning? What is so peculiar in the nervous synapses and cells that they are needed and exist in primitive or complex form in each living thing? Are they essential to make life possible?

The cosmos (meaning order in Greek) is not very orderly except for a few things like day and night and the lunar phases. I am not sure that simpler nervous systems are aware of order in these phases. Meteorites fall in an extremely random and disorderly way. Suns are formed and disintegrate in a way that does not really fit the notion of order. At the other microscopic extremity there is equal randomness and lack of order. Nobody can predict which atom will break up in radium, or any other radioactive material. In any domain of the material world, gases, liquids, or whatever we may choose, nothing is predictable, orderly, stable, and invariant for any one of the molecules or atoms. No wind, sun, earthquake, or typhoon lives an orderly existence.

Nervous structures do look for order, and find it when and wherever it exists and make one where it does not exist. Only a very complex nervous assembly, consisting of such a great number of units as there are in most living creatures, needs consistency and constancy of environment. Primitive nervous systems do not play tennis, nor do they swing from one branch to another thirty feet away. Primitive systems are slower and are not so dependent on organizing invariants. All living creatures are smaller and weaker than their grown-ups, some for shorter some for longer intervals of time. Weak organisms need a more or less constant consistent world so that they can learn and grow into strong organisms. The organism is in itself quite a world of microbeings which needs constancy, order, invariance, homeostasis if it is to exist.

It is a platitude to say that only a brain can think, abstract, dream, remember, and so on. A nervous system introduces order into the random, constantly changing stimuli, impinging or arriving through the senses to the system. Moreover the living organism itself moves incessantly and the nervous system has to arrange the mobile changing world, and its own mobility, to make some sense of this whirling turmoil. If nothing ever repeats itself how could we learn?

Now, the most unexpected means to achieve this Herculean feat is movement. The movement of the living organism is essential to form stationary and repetitive events in the changing, moving environment; for if we find dead matter and motionless vegetation our senses still perceive moving impressions, since a living organism moves and is never completely stationary before it is really dead.

Professor Heinz Von Foerster from the Biological Computer Laboratory, University of Illinois, who nourishes similar ideas told me and my students in San Francisco the following story:

Henri Poincaré published a paper in 1887 explaining that the image of three dimensional space on the retina has only two dimensions, nor is the formation of the image on the retina uniform as it is in space. Awareness of the third missing dimension results from convergence of the two eyes and accommodation which is, in fact, a muscular sensation. Awareness of direction involves movement of the head.

The head movements need the adjustment of the eyes. Three-dimensional pictures would not be perceived with a stationary head and eyes. I have since read Poincaré's book, *Science and Hypothesis,* published in English by Dover. He shows that movement is involved in our perception of space, and our choice of Euclidean geometry. It is a fascinating book and is worthwhile reading today, as it is original and new—the thinking of a genius.

I cannot refrain from recalling yet another example of Poincaré's acumen. In those days most of the work on brain physiology consisted of removing a piece of brain, observing the affected function, and thus locating that function in the brain.

Poincaré thought this method was not sufficiently scientific, and he doubted the conclusion. His argument was that binocular tridimensional vision is affected every time a person loses his right eye, but it would be faulty to conclude that the three-dimensional function is located in the right eye.

A Swiss ski instructor, Mr. Kohler if I remember correctly, persuaded some of his pupils to participate with him in an experiment. He was interested to find out what would happen to us if our brain saw the outside world as it is on the retina and not as it exists. As everybody knows, the eye lens, like any other lens, inverts the image on the retina. A standing person has his head at the bottom of the retina and his feet at the top. Mr. Kohler gave all his participants a pair of glasses which inverted the image on the retina. To begin with, they all saw everything, as expected, upside down. The first hours were very difficult. They could not move freely or do anything without slowing down and trying to make sense of what they saw. Then something unexpected happened. Everything on the body and its immediate vicinity began to look as before but everything that was not touched continued to be inverted. Gradually, as they groped and touched whilst moving around to attain the satisfaction of normal needs, objects further afield began to appear normal. The glasses were not removed throughout the experiment. In a few weeks everything looked the right way up, and they could all do everything without any special attention or care. In the end, snow began to fall again and Mr. Kohler saw through the window the flakes rising from the earth and moving upward. He went out, stretched out his hands, and felt snow falling on them. He then turned his palms upward and, of course, snow fell on them. After only a few trials he saw the snow falling instead of rising.

There are other experiments with inverting glasses. One, carried out in the United States, concerned two people, one sitting in a wheelchair and the other pushing it, both fitted with the special glasses. The one who moved around by pushing the chair began to see normally and was able to find his way without groping after a few hours, while the one sitting continued to see everything the wrong way.

Does a newborn baby see the right way up from the start, or does he actually have to touch things in order to be able to interpret the impression received to fit his checking sense—his touch? I, for one, suspect that movement plays an important role in forming my objective world. And if my suspicion is not altogether wrong, movement may be necessary to all living things to enable them to form their objective exterior world, and perhaps even their objective internal world. We rarely stop to ask ourselves whether we are the adult realization of the program of our genetic code (DNA) alone. It is the spermatozoa that start the process. The DNA will select the changes to fit the code from a multitude of possible alternatives. We know that the realization of the program never happens without the growth of the organism that bears the genetic code. Being born and growing never happen without at least one observer or witness—the one that gives birth to the organism. However, as yet no living organism is known outside a gravitational field. To sum up, a genetic program is incorporated into a body which grows from two cells, in an environment that contains unavoidable gravitation and witnesses. None of these items can alone, by any stretch of the imagination, form a living being able to grow and become adult.

All mammals have a form, a skeleton, muscles, a nervous system, and are born to parents. Men are born into a culture, a human society located somewhere on earth. The earth exercises a gravitational force which is never interrupted and which cannot be screened. It is permanent and practically the same everywhere. Though the bones are living matter since they grow and can regenerate when injured they are, nevertheless relatively speaking, inert matter. They cannot change their form, position, or configuration without the pulls exerted on them by muscles. There are large and small muscles, striated and smooth muscles. All of them can only contract and stop contracting, whereby they recover their initial length in preparation for the next contraction. Muscles do not contract without impulses issued by the nervous system to make them do so. This is not quite true, as in the early stages of development of the embryo the heart muscles, in fact, contract in a special rhythm, usually more rapid than in the adult, long before any nerves reach the heart. There is obviously another mechanism to make muscles contract.

There are two major kinds of muscular fibres; white fibres and red fibres. These differ not only in color, but also in the time they maintain their contractions as well as the rate of them. The muscles contract so that the bones can close and open articulations, and the two kinds of activity are said to be antagonistic. It goes without saying that in the adult the muscles, per se, have no say in their contraction, or ceasing contraction which is, of course, relaxation.

The nervous system distributes impulses which activate the muscles and are the cause of all movement. It is a very complex structure producing an immense variety of patterns of muscular activity, from reflex knee jerks, tremor, clonus, to smooth intentional movement. Every alteration of the configuration of the skeleton is produced by a particular pattern of impulses dispatched to the muscles. The time of arrival to the different muscles and the amount of their contractions, regulated by special mechanisms, are taken into account so that fine, delicate, strong, sudden, gradual, and a large variety of other movements are performed by the skeleton. Movements are produced in space and at different moments in time. The movements of the skeleton carrying with it the muscles and the nervous system occur in space, at different times, and in an environment which is also a social human environment and very rarely otherwise. The movements displace the organism. What we call the organism consists of the skeleton, the muscles, the nervous system, and all that goes to nourish, warm, activate, and rest the whole of it.

These movements produce the displacement of the entire organism and change its configuration for different activities which, in turn, affect all different sorts of environment to provide the necessities of the organism. There is, thus, a continuously changing environment with a continuously changing organism, interacting without stopping so long as there is life in the organism. The different environments affect the organism which changes so as to act and react effectively to the environment. We have, then, a closed loop of four elements: skeleton, muscles, nervous system, and environment. These four elements interact from birth until death and there are feedback and feedforward operations all along the loop. At birth, the link organism-environment is largely passive. By and by, it becomes less and less passive. Gradually, it becomes more and more intentionally active. Were there no gravitational field the whole scheme would be totally different. The muscles would be superfluous. The skeleton would be entirely different. There would be no posture characteristics of any animal. The entire energy scheme would be altered. Bones would not need to be able to withstand compression. The velocity of movement would be altogether changed. In fact, it would be nothing that we can really conceive in its entirety. As it is, movement is the best clue to life. Ever since man could speak he has classified all existing things according to their movement in the gravitational field. Vegetation is everything that can move only passively from side to side following the flow of water, or air, otherwise the growth is vertical. Light may affect vertical growth in its own direction. Living things can displace themselves in different ways, and each way has a class named after the way of movement. The swimming ones are fishes. The flying ones are birds. The gliding ones are snakes. The wriggling ones are worms. There are jumping ones, crawling ones, climbing ones, the ones that walk on all fours, and we who walk upright. Movement seems to have preoccupied man since he can first remember himself.

Since movement is of such importance to the living cell or assembly of cells making up any living organism, it is certainly something that happens not by chance alone. Most of the organism—the skeleton, the muscles, and the nervous system—is preoccupied with movement in our environment. And this is so complex that most living things are so constructed that they need some personal individual apprenticeship in practically all species, be they fishes, birds, animals, apes, or men. The amount of apprenticeship varies from a few seconds, to a few minutes, to many years. Some of the herd animals, especially the bovines, horses, zebras, and their like seem to be able to follow the herd almost immediately they are dropped by the mother cow, mare, or whatever she may be called. A calf dropped—a giraffe calf drops from rather high —will make an attempt or two to get on its feet immediately its umbilical cord is chewed, and it is licked all over. When the second or third attempt is successful, the calf will follow the cow on sand, gravel, slippery wet grass no matter whether it is on level, ascending, or descending ground. It can not only do everything necessary to cling to the herd, but if it happens to slide or stumble it can right itself. If one thinks of the complexity and ingenuity necessary to construct something similarly efficient one can only realize what is involved in this extraordinary ability to move without previous experience and with so little apprenticeship.

Think of the Chamonix or other mountain goats where the kids are born on high rocks. The kids right themselves on their feet and then have to leap from one sharp edge to another without a marked previous apprenticeship. Obviously all the connections, the wiring in of the nervous systems of these animals must be made before they are born. In short, it is the species that has handed down the learning, the evolving, the reflex organization, the instinct that enables them to survive in precarious conditions. However, most birds, dogs, kittens of all sorts, even tiger kittens, have to have some kind of coaching by their parents to finish the wiring in; establishing the functioning patterns of their nervous systems. What makes this pattern reliable, autonomous, or automatic is an apprenticeship of a few weeks.

When we pass in review many of the species it becomes evident that the lower the species' place on the ladder of evolution the more complete is the wiring in of the nervous system at birth. The connections of the synapses, neurons, or whatever are ready and the apprenticeship is shorter the lower the species are on the ladder. In man, we see the extreme end of this process. The human infant has the longest apprenticeship of all the species, to my knowledge. Although everything necessary to maintain life and growth is already connected in the nervous and glandular systems at birth, the specific human functions are not wired in at all. No baby was ever born who could speak, sing, whistle, crawl, walk upright, make music, count or think mathematically, tell the hour of the day or night, or know what it is to be late. Without a very long apprenticeship lasting several years none of these functions has ever been observed. As far as these specifically human functions or activities go, the connections or the wiring in of the neural structures have advanced already in the womb but compared with those of the adult they are non-existent.

It is the individual personal experience or apprenticeship that is necessary, and without it the baby will not be a human being. It is as if there were no inherited learning in the human species whatsoever. The "lower" animals have phylogenetic learning, or inherited evolved learning of their species. The "higher" animal learns through his own individual ontogenetic experience. The "lower" and "higher" have little meaning other than referring to the complexity, and our way of constructing the ladder of evolution. Almost all the lower animals can do things that the highest can only learn to understand, but can never do without prolonged learning, and then can only imitate, usually with a great variety of auxiliary instruments or structures. It may not be superfluous to repeat here that only the nervous tissues and systems are capable of conceiving as well as performing or realizing. The tendency to repetition leads in the end to repetitive constancy and order. Most happenings are ruled by chance and are so disorderly that most goings-on are not predictable. We make the laws of nature by singling out the parts of events we cannot change or to which we can add what we consider order. Newton made order in an impressive array of disorderly falling bodies by introducing the notion of cosmic gravitation. The neural substance that organizes order in its own functioning also makes order in its environment which in turn improves the orderliness of neural function. The neural substance organizes itself and thereby selects and alters the incoming messages from the environment into invariant sets to make repetition possible. It takes many continuously changing messages from the environment before the organism succeeds in perceiving them as unchanging entities. So great is the ability of the nervous system that it creates order where instruments made of any other matter will register a blur of continuous variations. Just think of taking a photograph of a greyhound running toward you while you are sitting on a galloping horse.

We can understand each other while a fan or air-conditioner is making so much background noise that no recorder without a human expert will reproduce an intelligible record of what we have said. We have no difficulty extracting invariant order out of many changing interferences. In anything we see, hear, smell, or feel we actively organize ourselves so as to be impressed by those invariant sets that make us cope with the disorder in ourselves, and outside in our environments, personal, social, spatial, and temporal. Children can learn a language in a room in which several different languages are being taught. This works when the teachers and the children are interested in learning. We see a box of matches as having an invariable size and form, but a camera, a telescope, binoculars, or any instrument used in science will see the box as a dot if we move it far enough away. If we see it from a corner, we still see a "square" box—not so the instruments. Our nervous system creates invariants wherever it is expedient.

Suppose we make a machine that incorporates a skeleton, muscles, organs, and also a brain. Would a brain like that speak English or Turkish? It would not know how to speak at all. Would a brain like that be able to read, to think mathematics, to listen to or create music? Could it make an IBM machine or a microphone? Of course not. When the brain comes into the world it is fit to do only what any animal brain can do: it attends to breathing, to digestion, to the automatic processes of the body. Beyond that, we must wire in that brain to relate to the environment into which it comes. At the outset, the brain does not even know how to stand. It cannot read or whistle, or tap-dance or skate or swim. The brain must be adjusted and connected in order to fully function.

Assume that I am looking at a microphone. When my eyes look at it, I identify the image. Actually there is no image of a microphone in my brain. There is an image of the microphone on my retina. From the retina, the image from each eye is separated into two parts and projected on four different parts of the cerebral cortex, which actually has no real image of a microphone. However, the function of seeing evokes in my mind the thing that I see with my eyes. The brain goes through a type of schooling that "wires" it into objective reality. Reality, therefore, encompasses the environment and the body itself.

The mind gradually develops and begins to program the functioning of the brain. My way of looking at the mind and body involves a subtle method of "rewiring" the structures of the entire human being to be functionally well integrated, which means being able to do what the individual wants. Each individual has the choice to wire himself in a special way. However, the way we do it now is almost completely futile, alienating us from our own capacity to have our own feelings.

Each person is born as a humanoid, a human animal. The newborn baby can swallow, suck, digest, excrete, and maintain body temperature like any other animal. What makes us different from animals is that humanoids can develop into homo sapiens, human beings with intelligence, knowledge, and awareness.

Summary

Among the many roads there are high roads. All men have curiosity—a sensory world that helps to find the "high road" important to every one of us. The ways home (the shelter from radiation for cells) for safety must be familiar. Otherwise, it is too slow to go home, and very uncertain. So "territory" is a word for something as old as life itself. What does home mean to you? Where do you go when tired or hurt? Are there other choices? How did we come by those we have? How do we act, adapt, or adjust ourselves? Has learning anything to do with this? What sort of learning? How do we do it?

ON LEARNING

Organic learning is essential. It can also be therapeutic in essence. It is healthier to learn than to be a patient or even be cured. Life is a process not a thing. And, processes go well if there are many ways to influence them. We need more ways to do what we want than the one we know—even if it is a good one in itself.

Organic learning begins in the womb and continues during the whole of the individual's period of physical growth. Other forms of learning directed by teachers take place in schools, universities, and colleges where there are numerous students. As well as similarities in these two types of learning there are essential differences between them, some of which are very subtle.

An adult, realizing he encounters inherent difficulties achieving what others manage with apparent ease, usually feels something is wrong with him. Parents and teachers alike will encourage such a person to make greater efforts, believing that some form of laziness is inhibiting the learning. Sometimes increased application does result in a form of improvement, but it is not rare to find people who discover later in life that the changes were only superficial.

The number of adults who experience difficulties in their social life, i.e. marital, professional, or body inadequacy, can be estimated when we think of the number of methods and techniques available today to help such people. How many practice Zen, meditation, psychoanalysis by several different methods, psychodrama, biofeedback, hypnotism, dance therapy, and so on. There must be something like fifty or more known therapies for people who do not feel medically ill, but are discontented with their sensations and performance. In all the methods we have to help people in distress they do a considerable amount of learning. So we have to understand the different kinds of learning before we can see the importance of yet another method created and used by me.

For human beings, learning, and especially organic learning, is a biological, not to say physiological, necessity. We learn to walk, speak, sit on chairs the Indian way, the Japanese way, read, write, paint, play instruments, whistle. We have practically no instincts for eating and drinking, and we live as much by our cultural and racial environment as by our biology.

The nervous system of an embryo, a baby, a child is wired in, so to speak, through the senses, feelings, and kinesthetic sensations caused by the spatial, temporal, filial, and social, as well as cultural, environment. But, organic juvenile learning, involving a complex structure and various associated functions and taking several years, cannot be without errors and failures in perfection. Organic learning is individual, and without a teacher who is striving for results within a certain time, it lasts as long as the learner keeps at it.

This organic learning is slow, and unconcerned with any judgment as to the achievement of good or bad results. It has no obvious purpose or goal. It is guided only by the sensation of satisfaction when each attempt feels less awkward as the result of avoiding a former minor error which felt unpleasant or difficult. Pushed by parents or anyone to repeat any initial success the learner may regress, and further progress can be delayed by days, even weeks, or not occur at all.

Development of bodily structures coincides with the

learner's attempt to function in his environment. The baby will only continue rolling from side to side as long as no nervous structures linking the eyes, ears, and neck muscles have matured sufficiently to make other movement possible. I am not going to deviate from our immediate purpose by talking about the ripening of the palidum for primitive crawling, the striated body, or the future development of the brain for further progress in body movement.

The ripening of the nervous structures and their linkage in patterns will be affected by any of the body's attempts to function, and vice versa. Learning may therefore progress to perfection, become deviated, or even regressed before the next ripening will coincide with another attempt at function. Time presses on in growth and anything not attempted in its own time may remain dormant for the rest of the learner's life. If he has not learned to speak before a certain time he will never speak well for the whole of his life. In organic learning there is no appointed teacher, although the child may learn through his mother by accepting or rejecting her example. He will choose different acts from different sources as it happens to please his senses.

Scholastic learning with teachers in charge is perhaps the greatest human achievement and is the source of our successes as social beings as well as some of our shortcomings. The teacher knows what he is teaching and where he leads his students. The students know what they learn and when they have achieved the learning to the teacher's satisfaction. Their training is strewn with exercises designed to reach the desired goal to the teachers satisfaction. We can learn medicine, engineering, law, and similar subjects this way.

Such learning has a prescribed curriculum which the group has to go through by the end of an allotted period. A few individuals will be successful with all the teachers. These are the students at high schools and universities whose organic learning was good enough. Some will never make it and will remain at the bottom of the class, whilst others will achieve a modicum of learning sufficient not to be rejected for the next class at the beginning of the following year. It goes without saying that this description does not give due credit to those teachers in each generation to whom we owe most of our progress. We owe to them also some of the best human beings in the past and in the present.

Scholastic practice is responsible for parents beliefs, and understanding of learning. It seems that well-meaning parents interfere with organic learning to the point that many therapies trace the real start and development of most dysfunctions back to the parents. These findings are so general that one would think we would be better off if we never had parents at all. Orphans fare even worse; they are reared by people who have the same attitude as the parents about what is correct, but care less. They think willpower is the real way to achieve correct functioning, and consider that repeated attempts will ensure excellency. In fact, exercising for the correct final state only produces familiarity and makes any errors habitual. The person who feels dysfunction is helpless. He tries to do the correct thing, knows that he fails, and is convinced that something is fundamentally wrong with him. When we consider music, painting, writing, thinking, feeling, or loving, we are inclined to believe that Beethoven, Bach, Picasso, Michelangelo, Tolstoy, Joyce, Wittgenstein, Einstein, Dirac, or Dante used their own personal ways and methods rather than what had been taught to them and was thought correct.

Teachers in front of classes of students rely on words to make their pupils understand and grasp the subject. This seems the unavoidable method of instruction but it does not mean that there are no serious drawbacks in the system. The laws of nature as taught now have become so habitual in our thinking that we do not stop to consider what they actually mean. Science does not discover the laws of nature but rather the laws of human nature. Discovery of how our brain functions may take many centuries yet just because we look outside for its manifestations. Take the example of a triangle, which is one of the simplest geometrical figures. Everything we know about triangles from before Euclid and until today is actually contained in the simple figure we can draw outside of ourselves on a piece of paper; but, bisectors, perpendiculars, medians, inscribed circles, and circumscribed circles, the area, and the different shapes of triangles are the product of our brain and are not the laws of the triangle drawn there on the paper. It was either Pascal or Descartes who, by the age of thirteen, had completed his understanding of geometry and rediscovered what we know of it without having discovered any laws of nature except those of his own thinking. It takes something like thirty to forty years to become familiar with any "law" of importance, which is any thought of real originality, such as the periodic table of Mendeleev, color photography, relativity, and the double spiral in genetics; by then, appreciation of its significance and clearer understanding of its application may be possible. These things, of course, have something "out there" in our environment, and our brains have been wired in from inception until this very moment by the outside impinging on them, through our senses. With no senses at all, what sort of laws would there be in the world outside us? Our brains cannot function without an external world, without muscles and bones which are necessary only because self-propulsion is fundamental to animal life.

The "natural" numerical series from 1 to 2 to 3 to infinity is perhaps an even more convincing example of how laws are a study of the ways our brains function, as this law is claimed to be found only in "objective" reality. There are odd and even numbers in the series, and their distribution is peculiar. There are primes, and their distribution is still different. Also, there are Pythagorean trios: $3^2 + 4^2 = 5^2$, since $9 + 16 = 25$, etc. There are in the series enough laws to fill a thick book. Now where, in the world outside us, is the series and its laws? The series exists only when we write it down, or imagine it, which is how our brains were wired in in the first place. Obviously, all the laws of the natural series are the laws of function of the brain more than anything else. Organic learning is lively and takes place when one is in a good mood, and works at short intervals. The attitude is less serious, and the spells are more erratic compared with a day of academic learning or study.

It may be good to tell an anecdote here. A few years ago I had the good fortune to be introduced to Margaret Mead by Jean Houston and Bob Masters in the Serendipity Restaurant in New York. When we were seated at our table, Margaret Mead said she would first like to ask a question to see if my answer rang a bell with her. During her anthropological studies, she had returned to the same island for more than twenty years, yet she had not been able to teach the inhabitants or their children certain foot movements—a kind of hopping from one foot to the other, in spite of the fact that the people were good hunters and fishermen. I was unable to give a precise answer without knowing a little more about the movement, but I told her, in my view the fault or interference most probably arose from an inhibition or taboo affecting crawling in early childhood. She exclaimed she believed that I was on the right track. She then told me that the people of that island do not allow their babies to touch the ground on all fours for fear that they will grow bestial. Crawling is therefore eliminated altogether. That meeting was the start of a friendship which lasted until her death.

A person reviewing his organic learning in order to assess the parts that have matured to the full extent of his genetic endowments must remember that there are few intellectual processes in which thinking can be divorced from the awareness of being awake. Being awake means that we know whether we are standing, sitting, or lying. It means that we know how we are oriented relative to gravity. When thinking in words, even subliminally, we are logical and think in familiar patterns, in categories that we have thought, dreamed, read, heard, or said sometime before. Learning to think in patterns of relationships, in sensations divorced from the fixity of words, allows us to find hidden resources and the ability to make new patterns, to carry over patterns of relationship from one discipline to another. In short, we think personally, originally, and thus take another route to the thing we already know.

To my mind, learning that allows further growth of the structures and their functioning is the one that leads to new and different ways of doing things I already know how to do. This kind of learning increases my ability to choose more freely. Having only a single mode of action means my choice is limited to simply acting or not acting.

This may not be as simple as it sounds. We all turn our heads to the right if we intend to look to the right, and our shoulders will also participate in the twisting to the right. Looked at from the point of view of organic learning, moving the head, the eyes, and the shoulders in the same direction is the most primitive, simplest mode of action learned in early childhood. The nervous system is capable of other patterns of movement, say the eyes to the left while the head and shoulders go to the right. There are actually six different possibilities. Try any one of them which is not familiar to you. Go very, very slowly so that you can realize where you move head, eyes, and shoulders while "differentiating" them from the only pattern you know. What for? Just see what happens to you when you have succeeded in a novel pattern a few times and have made it more or less as fluent as the familiar one. You will feel taller, lighter, you will breathe better and have a sense of euphoria which you may never have known before. Your entire intentional cortex will work with such a quality of self-direction as you always felt it could.

Imagine now that you learn to differentiate and repattern

most of yourself, that is, most of your activity. Your intentional cortex will lose all the compulsive patterns with no alternatives and you will find yourself actually acting in many new ways. To facilitate your task, sit or even lie to begin with. When the pressure distribution on the soles of the feet is removed, as when lying, the intentional cortex is freed from the standing pattern all through the body. This may be the first time in your life that new alternative patterns can be formed in the cortex connections and affect the performance of your self.

This kind of learning, such as you will achieve if you try and follow me is also the kind of learning produced by Awareness through Movement lessons where the accent is put not on which movement you deal with but on how you direct yourself doing it.

Consider such a small thing as the ability to differentiate the movement of the third finger in both hands—the annular fingers which seem of no importance at all. Well, humanity is divided by this into two groups: those who can play or make music and those who can only buy tickets to concerts, or hi-fi equipment. For we can live a "normal" life with annulars participating in the movements of the neighboring medius and auriculars. But the fiddle, the flute, the piano and most other instruments demand the independent movement of the annulars and that they should have the same degree of differentiation as the index finger or thumb. This is a small example of what amazing potential can be discovered in everyone if structures and patterns of functions are dealt with methodically in this way. To master such skills is not easy, but education and learning could undergo a qualitative change by popularizing a system such as this.

Differentiation is a word, and a difficult one at that. The importance of such an action is that it increases the number of choices available for what we already know one way of doing. When no alternatives are available, we may be well if we are lucky. But if we are not, we will feel apprehension, doubt, even anxiety from time to time. When there is no choice of choices, we feel that we cannot change even though we know that we engender our own misery. We think, "I am no good. I cannot do otherwise because I am like that."

A wide variety of choices enables us to act differently and appropriately in similar but different situations. Our responses may be stereotyped but fit the terrain. We can use ourselves to better our lives. We cannot function satisfactorily if our thinking, senses, and feelings do not affect our acts or responses. Therefore your acts and responses must contain, even in your expectation or imagination, feelings of satisfaction, and pleasurable achievement or outcome. This makes therapies effective. By the end of this book, you will have at least some means that you can use yourself.

Summary

Humans have the most complex central nervous system (CNS) of all mammals. All nervous systems are built for learning phylogenetically, as in more primitive creatures. The human CNS is the best structure on earth for individual (ontogenetic) learning. The external world affects our senses and our brains. So much so that if we are born into an environment with any one of the three thousand languages, our brains will be so organized that we learn and know only that one language. Our ears, mouths, and everything else will be formed to speak that language as it is spoken in that environment.

BIOLOGICAL
ASPECTS
OF POSTURE

Stability is nice. It also means difficulty to initiate movement as well as difficulty to be moved. A boxer on the ground is saved only by the rule not to be destroyed before he is unstable again. He will then be able to move to attack and move to avoid being knocked down again. Stability (when one is protected) increases the feeling of safety. Instability means risk but easy mobility. Both are biologically important. Becoming addicted to one of them makes one unsafe for lack of choice.

When we see one of the tremendous buildings in the great cities of the world, we do not usually think about its foundations. We may also be surprised to find empty flats or apartments in a building that looks like a busy hive most of the time. But if a strong earthquake shakes the city, then the foundations of the building that grew to be a skyscraper will decide whether or not it will stand and be repairable, or will collapse beyond recovery. We began with a static structure, and in normal times we are concerned only with how the building can be used. When we have to consider dynamic balance or equilibrium under stress or trauma, then all these things become entirely different. It becomes important to know the depth, materials, and quality of the foundations, and the design and method of construction of the superstructure. We relate to human beings much as we do to static buildings so long as they stand up. Provided they function and do not complain more than is good for them and their society, then we do not think about how they are built and of what. We are not interested to know how they grew to be what they are. It matters little to their fellow men what sort of shocks they are able to take just to be shaken, compared with what will destroy them beyond repair. It obviously depends on the skill, experience, and ingenuity of the structural engineer as to which building will be repaired and which will be condemned.

In human beings, like in all living things, there is recovery from small shocks, injuries, and mishaps. When a person is shaken and the usual mysterious process of healing does not bring the person back to normal functioning, he is not condemned but he is helped back to recovery. An almost incredible number of helpers will deal with one pain and its localization, all of them oblivious that an individual, a human being, is in trouble. An example out of my own experience may make it clearer. A woman in her sixties complained of persistent acute pain in her lower abdomen above her pubis. She went to her general practitioner who ordered X-ray pictures and analysis of her blood and urine and all the usual things that a good conscientious doctor does. In the end he told her that he could find nothing wrong with her. Of course, her state of health was not what it was when she was twenty. However, considering her present age he could prescribe pain-killing pills, but the pain would probably improve by itself. The pain persisted and she returned to her doctor who then suggested that she see a gynecologist. The same procedure of examination, X ray, tests, occurred all over again and the same, "I can see nothing really wrong, but of course, you are not the same as when you were young." She pleaded that she could not sleep and that she found it hard to work, so it was decided that maybe an orthopedist should examine her pelvic and lumbar structures. The orthopedist, in his turn, repeated the X ray and the examination, and did everything a good conscientious orthopedist would do. No need now to tell you the familiar

story again. He answered her complaints by advising a neuro-
logical examination, and this was done, with a repetition of
the now rather boring, but inevitable result. To the poor lady's
complaint that she had suffered for over eight months and
could not attend to her daily duties, the neurologist advised
her to consult a psychiatrist as all the other experts, including
himself, could find no organic reason for her pains.

It turned out that while she was in a concentration camp in
Germany during the Second World War, she had lost a child.
When she was liberated at the age of nineteen, she knew of no
way of earning her livelihood, and was nursed by the French
after a nervous breakdown, before reaching a kibbutz in Israel. Within a few years she remarried, only to again lose both
her husband and son in the last Israeli war. She was a person
of extraordinary vitality, strengthened and matured by her
suffering, yet because she could no longer give birth, she felt
she was unfit to start life for the third time. Between us we
discovered that she felt her pain in the part of her body which
had caused her the most suffering.

The point I wish to make is that each of the people she
turned to treated only the one part of the woman that both-
ered her, and none of them dealt with her as a person. The
psychiatrist might have achieved a little more but he would
not have known whether or not there was an organic reason.
The woman was frightened by the idea of a psychiatrist, feeling that her sanity was doubted. I will, once you are in a
position to follow the bizarreries of my understanding of our
common lot, tell you how she recovered from her pains. If you
remember the dancing idea you may guess in principle how it
was done.

We are not a static building and to restore the good functioning of a human being is a much more delicate matter, neces-
sitating more fundamental knowledge of how we grow to function as we do, and greater information and insight to
understand what the person himself does not. After all, he is

a person like you and me. How is it that he is not conscious of the dynamics of his life, but rather sees himself as a kind of living machine that keeps on trying so long as there is vitality in it. In other words, his vitality is gone when he stops ticking. This is really not an explanation. It seems quite obvious that life is not static. It is a process continuing in time from the beginning and moving forwards to a future without limit. Everybody probably knows that life is a process, but not everybody knows that static equilibrium is not applicable to a process. When a static structure is knocked down the structure stays down. A living body, however, moving or inert, shows unexpected modes of reacting to being knocked down.

Systems made up of a great number of more elementary systems, or organisms made up of smaller living organisms are not thrown out of functioning just by being knocked about or down. They are ruled by laws that we have introduced or discovered. These laws govern large systems, living organisms, species, civilizations, and the like.

Let us look a little closer at what we know about dynamic equilibrium, or better, equilibrium of large systems in which activity and movement are the rule. A human being with a number of individual living cells, 2^{58}, is large even in astronomical terms, and qualifies to be considered a large system. The steel industry, ICI, and the Phillips of this world are large systems. A human being breaking a leg or an arm is only thrown a little back, he regresses to an inferior state of activity but is only knocked about. He will recover and most of the time will be able to continue developing. In a large system such as the ones we have mentioned, if a whole plant is destroyed the system will be thrown a little back, but will recover to continue its development. In dynamic equilibrium, the question is not standing or falling but how large is the shock that the system can receive before recovery of development becomes impossible. The greater the number of smaller systems that make up the large one, the greater is the likelihood of recovery and survival.

Le Chatelier, the great chemist, studied the problems of dynamic equilibrium of large systems. He showed that when such an equilibrium is disturbed there arise forces in the system itself, and not from outside, to restore it to normality. In human beings when there is a disturbance of equilibrium, say a temperature rise or a poisoning or an infection, internal forces will arise to restore the normal level of functioning, or homeostasis.

Human posture, in spite of the implications of the static "posting", is a dynamic equilibrium. A posture is good if it can regain equilibrium after a large disturbance. Take an empty bottle by the neck and deviate it slowly away from the vertical to the point where you can feel that when left alone the bottle's first tendency will be to move back to the upright position. The bottle, when released, will oscillate several times before friction will reduce the consecutive oscillations to nil and it will return to static equilibrium as it was before the disturbance. This is the simplest tangible example of internal forces arising in the moving, or dynamic equilibrium, to restore equilibrium. The example is somewhat of an oversimplification, for here the oscillations of the potential energy into kinetic and vice versa are the result of your deviating the bottle and of gravitation and are therefore not strictly internal forces arising in large systems.

Human upright standing, loosely referred to as posture, is not governed by the laws of static equilibrium. An unrestrained statue of a man or a woman, heavy as it may look, would topple over in a strong storm. Usually statues of humans have long rods under their feet which are imbedded in the support or pedestal and rooted to the stone with molten lead. The heavy head and trunk are at the top making the center of gravity rather high for good stability. The volume where the center of gravity is in our body is in the region of the third lumbar vertebra and is thus nearly four feet high. The center of gravity of changing configurations of a body is not a fixed point in the body.

It is more difficult to stand than to move. Young soldiers standing to attention on parade sometimes fall unconscious after prolonged immobility. Babies step precipitately forward long before they can stand without moving. We will have to return to the dynamics of human posture, as our nervous system, having evolved together with our skeleton and muscles in our gravitational field, is structured to deal with the dynamics of an erect body with a very high center of gravity. I would say that our nervous system, as well as our body, works to restore equilibrium rather than to keep it. The structure and the function of the nervous system provide the principles and the means to guide us to efficient use of ourselves. This is essential if we are to learn to function in harmony with ourselves. Harmonious efficient movement prevents wear and tear. More important, however, is what it does to the image of ourselves and our relationship to the world around us.

I have discovered, through personal experience, a phenomenon which is now one of the foundations of my teaching. I believe that I have already mentioned that I badly injured a knee while playing soccer football in my younger years. It was a severe injury and I was incapacitated for many months. The healthy leg had to work overtime and lost much of its former flexibility and nimbleness. One day I slipped on an oily patch on the pavement while hopping on the only leg that functioned. I felt my knee nearly spraining but it finally slipped back into position. I hopped home. I then had to climb two flights of stairs and at the end of it was glad to lie down. Gradually I felt my good leg stiffen and thicken with synovial waters. My original injured knee was still strongly bandaged and sufficiently painful to prevent me standing on the foot. I hopped around, therefore, on the leg which I had nearly sprained, thinking that probably I would soon not be upright at all, and would have to stay in bed. I fell asleep with a heavy heart.

When I woke up and tried to see whether I could manage to reach the bathroom without help, I was surprised to find that I could actually stand on the foot which I had been unable to use since the original troubles. The trauma of the good knee had somehow made the injured leg more usable than before; in fact, had it been as good as it was then I would not have had to hop. I thought that I might be turning insane. How could a leg with a knee that had prevented me standing on it for several months suddenly become usable and nearly painless? This happened, moreover, when the quadriceps of the leg had nearly vanished, as is usual in severe injury of the meniscus, and the thigh was visibly thinner. It seemed to me that the vanished quadriceps had become suddenly toneful enough to allow me to stand on the foot. I had not heard of such a miraculous change in an injured knee when physical anatomical abnormalities were clearly to be seen on the X-ray pictures. Cold sweat covered my face and I did not know whether I was awake or dreaming. I held onto the furniture and tried to move. There was no doubt. I put my weight on the bad leg while the one on which I had been hopping became auxiliary. The old injured leg would not straighten completely, and I leaned on the toes rather than the heel, but there was no doubt that it supported the bulk of my weight.

For fear of ridicule I spoke to nobody, and remained unsure of what had happened. I was convinced there was something mentally wrong with me, as the healing of the knee in hours was unthinkable, and yet the mishap to the good knee had improved the sick one. Many years later, on reading Professor Speransky's book *A Basis for the Theory of Medicine* it dawned on me that changes like the one I had experienced can be understood only by referring to the nervous system. I had thought so myself but did not dare to say or act upon such an insane idea. Inhibition of one part of the motor cortex can alter the neighboring symmetrical point even to excitation, or reduce its inhibition. Pavlov maintained that a point of excitation on the cortex is of necessity surrounded by a zone of inhibition. At the time of the injuries it seemed to me a wild idea to even consider it possible to effect a change in an anotomical structure through an alteration in the functioning of the brain, which involves negligible energy, compared with one in the skeleton. Later I gathered stories of many similar happenings with other people. I asked Dr. Spitz, a senior dentist who taught a generation of orthodontists, whether she had ever found that a patient complaining of an infected tooth on one side of the jaw could only chew again on that side suddenly after a traumatic accident to the other side. She remembered three cases in her long career, but she admitted she never mentioned them to anyone else, but rather tried to forget them as she could find no rational explanation. In hemiplegias, the other side shows increased tonus almost at the same time as the quadriceps on the paralyzed leg begins to vanish and the leg becomes thinner. Professor Speransky became Director of the Pavlov Institute after Pavlov's death and he gathered from medical doctors all over Russia stories of similar phenomena to the ones he observed himself. After an injection made on one arm there appeared at the corresponding point on the other arm changes which were the inverted picture of the injection and the oedema around it. He found no explanation possible outside of one involving the nervous system.

I had the privilege of Karl H. Pribram's frequent presence at my San Francisco course, and on one occasion when he was answering questions from the audience, I asked him if he knew of any explanation for my observation that touching repeatedly the inside of the ear produced a sensation of warmth in the corresponding hand and foot. Dilatation of the capillaries and increased blood supply are governed by the autonomic nervous system and there is none, so far as I know, in the ear. Professor Pribram, who was a brain surgeon at the beginning of his illustrious scientific career, told us that he had had a case of brain surgery in the region of the ear and while operating he had noticed perspiration around the lips of his patient. He later carried out some research to elucidate how this could be, as there are no autonomic, sympathetic or parasympathetic innervations known in the region, of the ear. He published a paper twenty-five years ago which answered my questions.

We need a more imaginative scientific approach to understand the whole interrelated functions of all aspects of ourselves, rather than just being content with some idea of localized function. It is a very complex problem and we must prepare for more than one surprise before we have the foundations even on which to construct a building of knowledge and clear understanding.

We are now ready for a closer look at posture. All animals have a way of using themselves in the field of gravitation, but these movements are first exploratory and then in action they appear to be alert but also attentive. Using oneself is first of all displacing oneself, which is usually performed by altering the configuration of the body. Between one displacement and the next there is always a moment where the body is, practically speaking, not changing position significantly. This moment of relative immobility is characteristic for each species, including man: it is the specific characteristic of a given body. Whatever displacement there is of the whole body, or any more stationary changes of configuration of its parts, the animal must pass through the point of practical immobility. This point is the animal's posture.

An animal's posture can be likened to the "posture" of a moving or oscillating pendulum. Whatever the oscillation is, large or small, the pendulum always passes through the position of immobility, which we can again consider as posture. No oscillation can start from any configuration other than the vertical, and with each oscillation it passes through its "posture" configuration.

This analogy needs an important correction which will be forthcoming. We can look at the matter another way. All species of animals have a characteristic form of posture, which usually we think of as standing, although dynamically this is the configuration of the body from which any act is made. Before lying, running, swimming, copulating, or whatever act, the animal returns to the standing posture. And in most activities, the animal passes through its standing configuration before finally recovering it. When we sit, we get there from standing. When we lift, throw, jump, swim, or do anything, we start and finish by standing. If we consider the trajectory of the center of gravity between acts, it will of necessity, pass through the point where it is in standing. It will start from that localization in the trajectory and will return there once the activity ceases. I consider, therefore, posture to be that part of the trajectory of a moving body from which any displacement will, of necessity, start and finish. This is considering posture dynamically, or from the view point of movement which is the most general characteristic of life. It is static immobility, in the same place and in the same configuration, which generally either endangers or ends life. A dead animal abandons its characteristic posture and becomes a static configuration with little importance to life.

The essential correction to the pendulum analogy is that the pendulum is normally at its lowest possible position, just as the dead animal is. A "live" pendulum, just like a live animal, has its center of gravity at the highest possible position which is its characteristic start or finish of any displacement of itself. An inverted pendulum, say a sphere at the top of a stick, is what I call a "live" pendulum and makes the analogy closer since the center of gravity is then at its highest possible level when such a pendulum is stationary. This is possible, but it is as difficult as standing absolutely motionless.

The main differences between vegetation, which is also alive, and animal life, are modes of reproduction, modes of

nourishment, and modes of self-preservation. All these functions are achieved in animals with movement and changes of
position, in short, self-direction, while vegetation is compara-
tively immobile and statically rooted in the earth.

No animal can reproduce without mating, and both finding
a mate and mating need movement for them to occur at all.
Trees need no displacement of their bulk for similar results,
although some movement must happen, even in vegetation,
for reproduction to occur. The real difference is that in animals everything is largely dynamic and active, while vegetation is largely static, motionless, and passive.

Even faulty movement, the beginning and end of which is
still the characteristic posture of an animal, is not very complex and not very critical for reproduction. Crippled men and
women, even demented ones, are capable of moving sufficiently for reproduction. The time problem also is not critical
for them since it is a question of months and almost any
posture is good enough. Note, by the way, how laborious
speech is, for if you read the last few paragraphs you will
appreciate that I have avoided some of the very usual ways of
saying what I meant. The world is not just black and white,
but rather it has all possible shades of grey. It is easier to
understand one another when we are friends, and have established a common meaning of words, than to speak precisely
enough to be understood by those who do not wish to be led up
the garden path.

Taking nourishment is much more stringent and critical,
both in animals and vegetation. Only camels can, I believe,
survive a fortnight without water at all. I have not checked the
truth of this statement, only hearing it as commonplace
knowledge from Bedouins to whom the camel is almost as
important as themselves. If air is taken as nourishment,
which in fact it is, then it is obviously a very critical matter,
and it is a question of minutes whether or not we survive.
Taking in water, and then losing it through our breath and

sweat limit survival to a few days, except, maybe, for the camel and for some insects. Very few living things can exist more than a week without water. Food, in general, is a much less critical matter than air or water. In short, air, water, and even food are far more important for the survival of individuals than reproduction. The stuff that has to be taken in limits the existence of any animal to a few minutes, a few days, or just over a week or so. You can think for yourself about the survival of vegetation without moisture. Think of desert vegetation and of the effect of heat and frost on vegetation and on all living and moving animals and man.

Movement of the individual is, as regards temperature and nourishment, much more critical than reproduction in optimum conditions. However, life is limited by the lowest factor that will compromise survival. The lowest span of survival in matters of air, water, temperature, and nourishment is still measured in minutes or in days. This limit becomes also the limit of the reproductive function. In survival it is the lowest value that counts. Posture, as the configuration of the passage between the beginning and the end of any movement, is much more critical here than in reproduction. Healthy, mobile, alert, well-organized men and animals have a much better chance of survival than crippled or demented ones.

The third biological criterion of posture, as we have said, is self-preservation. This self-preservation aspect of posture is the most critical, and it may limit survival to a fraction of a second, or a few seconds in the lucky cases. As self-preservation is the most stringent measure of good movement, and good posture is a particular instance of good movement, it may help us to describe posture more accurately. Our hunting ancestors of only ten to fifteen thousand years ago so perfected their movement, and thus also their posture, that without claws or canines, without horns or hooves but just by sheer nimble and skilled movement, they enabled their descendants to become the rulers of the entire animal world. Wherever a group of humans settled, lions, snakes, boars, elephants—the fittest, strongest, heaviest animals—all had to recede, retreat, or perish because they were no match for the most precariously balanced and weakest of them all, the human hunter. To achieve the great variety of movement, the ability to halt, to change, or to continue, a fast brain had to develop apace. It is the inherent weakness of the human frame which certainly had something to do with humans getting together and developing tribal habits and clan life.

Human posture, at its best, is capable of such a wide range of movements that it makes man the king of the animal world, rather than the lion as we are taught in childhood. We have already seen that in man the center of gravity is very high because of the height of the head, shoulders, and the two arms. This structure can move easily only if it is used dynamically, and here again note the inherent difficulty of language and speech, for every movement is dynamic. To make the difference between dynamic and static use of yourself sensible to you, think of the stability of a body with a very low center of gravity. An object that has the bulk of the mass near the ground has to be primed with some form of power or energy before it can lift itself and rise while displacing itself: it is inherently slow to start any movement and it has to have enough energy supplied before it can move. A hydroplane is such a body and is like any aeroplane with landing wheels projecting from its belly. Such bodies are static in essence and they have to gather momentum after the supply of energy is switched on. The start is both clumsy and slow because of their structure.

When rising, the human body produces and stores energy, and on getting up to stand it raises its center of gravity to the highest level compatible with its structure. The human body normally stores in itself potential energy to start, in the gravitational field, any five of the six cardinal movements in space. To move down, right, left, forward, and backward it need only let go, for the energy has been stored by rising and will be transformed into kinetic energy by taking off the brakes, so to speak. The start of the movement is as fast as the intention to move, or in other words as fast as the intentions of the cortex or motor cortex.

One can see that human posture obeys the laws of dynamics even when motionless which is, thus, a particular point on the trajectory of movements. One can stop moving, continue in the original direction, or change to any other direction. A statically balanced (low center of gravity) body, when intending to move, has already too much inertia to overcome to be able to change direction.

Nervous conduction and muscular contraction work on the dynamic principle. They do not wait for energy to be switched on and supplied before they start. The nerve has energy stored for conduction and this energy is replenished afterwards ready for the next fire. Muscular fibres contract and afterwards refill with energy to be ready to contract again when triggered practically instantaneously, but not, of course, absolutely so.

Human posture has other advantages over that of animals. One, recognized long ago, is the liberation of the arms from weight-bearing. This, together with the swiftness of our brain, made the specially human power of manipulation a reality. Anthropoid apes have arms, hands, and muscles almost the same as man except for the thumbs which are unable to do what human thumbs can. The ability to oppose the tip of the thumb to the tip of any other finger is part and parcel of our manipulative dexterity, and this dexterity becomes staggering when contemplated. We can see a virtuoso playing the piano or performing on a violin with fingers moving faster than when we close our eyes in an emergency. To achieve the precision of a sixty-fourth of a second, or to produce a graded movement in strength is not often seen elsewhere.

The human posture is not simple nor is it easy to achieve.

It necessitates a long and demanding apprenticeship. The learning that each human being has to go through to achieve the best quality of functioning his structure permits is as remarkable as anything in nature.

Let us just look at what human posture can lead to. It can walk on a wire across Niagara Falls, which no cat can do even when balancing a pole on its snout. It can pole-vault, figure-skate, drum as a virtuoso, and bull-fight as a matador, who delays moving out of the way of a rushing maddened bull until the horns touch his red cape. It can ski-jump, juggle with ten objects in the air as Rasteli did, type three hundred words a minute, tap-dance, execute acrobatics on flying trapezes, dance Spanish flamencos, and become a whirling dervish. Pearl divers can stay under deep water for up to five minutes, and beam gymnasts like the Olympic gold-medalist can climb a balanced ladder and perform a one-hand-stand at the top. Then there is precision knife-throwing. Human movement and skill are a challenge to anybody's imagination. Just think of the skill of microwatch-making, screwing a screw that needs a microscope to be seen—what real finesse of movement! You will be able to extend this not inconsiderable list for yourself.

None of these skills is inborn. All of them need learning. How do we learn? What do we mean by learning? How is human posture learned? In the very rare cases where a human baby has been raised by animals outside human society, it walked on all fours like an ape most of the time, and only semi-erected itself for short spells. Things learned can be half-learned, and they can even be badly learned. Hence the great variety of human postures which are obviously not all as good, one as the other. We have already mentioned that our brain evolved alongside the learning of skills and we will return to this later.

Posture and attitude are so closely interdependent that most people complain of their posture while inwardly suspecting that there is something fundamentally wrong with their makeup. They believe that if they could have their posture "corrected," they would then change for the better. I believe that they are nearly right, but not quite. Posture can only be improved and not corrected. Only the concept of an ideal posture might be considered correct, but such a posture can exist only with an ideal brain and nervous system. Ideal models like this do not exist in reality. They can be approached more or less, but only approached, and there are almost as many directions of approach as radii in a circle.

Summary

When choice is reduced to only one movement or act without any alternatives, anxiety may be so great that we cannot even do the only possible movement. Put a ten-inch board on the floor and walk on it from one end to the other. Do so or just imagine yourself doing it visually or kinesthetically. Now, lift the board to about ten feet above the floor. Support it in the middle so that it is as rigid as the floor. Get on it and try to walk to the other end. Do so or imagine yourself doing it in the same way as indicated before. Feel or see how you produce the pattern of anxiety. Has anything to do with the pattern produced the fear of falling? Yet, some people have learned to walk over a precipice on a tree or on a beam. How would you set about doing that?

THE BODY PATTERN
OF ANXIETY

Anxiety can be a positive, useful phenomenon. It assures our safety from risking what we feel would endanger our very existence. Anxiety appears when deep in ourselves we know that we have no other choice—no alternative way of acting.

Straddle a board ten feet high and, with your feet dangling, shove yourself from one end to the other assisted by your hands on the board. No alternative stops you from using your creative imagination, as anxiety maintains your choice to the anxiety-producing alternative.

We cannot change at all. A Chinese will never change to be an Eskimo. But, there are changes that occur in us. Life is time-bound. It is a process of acting which needs internal organization of oneself to meet and affect the external changes. We learn to organize ourselves internally to meet challenges or challenge others. Our internal organization becomes faulty or poor with anxiety and produces poor and faulty moves and performs badly. The more our intents and performances are fixed, the less they are effective. Life is a process of time, and time cannot be fixed.

Without learning to know ourselves as intimately as we possibly can, we limit our choice. Life is not very sweet without freedom of choice. Change is very difficult with no alternatives in sight; we then resign ourselves to not dealing with our difficulties as if they were prescribed by heaven.

McDougall distinguishes fourteen different instincts: parental, sex, food-seeking, fear or escape, combat, constructiveness,
curiosity, repugnance, acquisitiveness, appeal (reciprocal of
parental instinct), herd instinct (gregariousness), self-asser-
tion, self-submission, and laughter. Pavlov thinks that there
is an instinct for freedom, that an animal objects to being tied
up or enclosed in a confined living space limiting its movements.

In physiology, an instinct is a complex integration of inborn,
unconditioned reflexes, as distinct from acquired or conditioned ones. The inborn reflexes are characteristic of the central nervous system of any whole class of animals: they are
inherited and their formation is, therefore, largely independent of individual experience. The notion of "instinct" is used
too loosely and is a source of many misconceptions.

Whatever instincts we may consider, we observe a remarkable thing—that only one of the instincts inhibits motion,
namely fear. An animal, when frightened, either freezes or
runs away. In either case there is a momentary halt. This halt
is produced by the first reaction to the frightening stimulus.
This is a violent contraction of all the flexor muscles, especially in the abdominal region, a halt in breathing, soon followed by a whole series of vasomotor disturbances such as
accelerated pulse, sweating, up to micturition and even defecation.

Bending the knee involves contracting the hamstring, a
flexor. The quadriceps muscle, an antigravity extensor, is the
antagonist, and thus is unable to contract sufficiently to
straighten the knee. The contraction of the flexors inhibits
their antagonistic extensors, or antigravity muscles: thus no
displacement occurs before this initial reaction is over. An
initial inhibition of the extensors goes together with all the
sensations that accompany fear. This is at first sight somewhat surprising. One would expect the first reaction to be such
as to withdraw the animal from danger as quickly as possible.

It is not so when the frightening stimulus is too near or too violent. The violent stimulus produces a general contraction of the flexors. Their initial contraction brings into operation the stretch reflex in the extensors which are thus capable of a greater effort when escaping. The initial flexor contraction, however, also enables the animal to freeze and simulate death if the danger is too near. All the other disturbances are produced by an increase of adrenalin content in the blood which is preparatory to possible violent effort of the heart and other muscles.

A newborn infant is practically insensitive to slow and small external stimuli. At birth he hardly reacts to light effects, to noise, to smell, and even moderate pinching. He reacts violently to immersion in very cold or hot water. Also if suddenly lowered, or if support is sharply withdrawn, a violent contraction of all flexors with halt of breath is observed, followed by crying, accelerated pulse, and general vasomotor disturbance, i.e. change of pulse, sweating, etc.

The similarity of the reactions of a newborn infant to withdrawal of support, and those of fright or fear in the adult is remarkable. This reaction to falling is present at birth, i.e. inborn and independent of individual experience. It is therefore right to speak of the instinctive reaction to falling.

Charles Darwin wrote a little book, *The Expression of the Emotions in Man and Animals.* In spite of the many inaccuracies, it is a very important book. I think it will be considered in time as the first reliable work in psychology. There are more facts in these few pages about emotions as seen in the living body than in many modern treatises on psychology. The attitude of fear, the sinking of the head, the crouching, the bending of the knees, etc. etc., as described by Darwin in this book, are but details of the general contraction of all flexor muscles compatible with the act of standing.

No reaction similar to that sensed as fear by the adult can be elicited in the newborn baby, except by sharply altering its position in space. When it begins to hear better, about three weeks after birth, it will respond also to very loud noises. It is a well-known fact that the stronger the stimuli the more they diffuse and irradiate in accordance with certain laws. Thus, if one hand is moderately pinched, that hand will be withdrawn reflexively. If the pinching is increased and the hand is prevented from moving, the opposite arm will twitch. If the stimulus becomes vigorous or violent, the legs and the whole body may be brought into action.

M. A. Minkovsky has found extreme irradiation, i.e. spreading of excitation, over the whole nervous system in human embryos. On scratching the foot, for example, the whole musculature, trunk, neck and head react. In newborn infants, the spreading of excitation is also greater than in the adult. Very loud noises excite the cochlear branch of the eighth cranial auditory nerve. The excitation flows over to the vestibular branch of the same nerve. This irradiation takes place not in the nerve, but at the first relays and possibly at still higher centers in the adult.

The eighth cranial nerve divides near the internal ear into two branches—the cochlear, concerned with hearing, and the vestibular, concerned with equilibrium. Reference to Testut or Shaefer's anatomy would show how closely and intricately these two branches are interconnected. The diffusion of strong impulses is, of course, not limited to the branches of the eighth cranial nerve. Higher up, at the superior olive, strong incitations, produced by very loud noises, will diffuse and excite the tenth cranial nerve, instrumental in holding breath.

Strong impulses from the vestibular branch will diffuse in the same way to the superior olive, and will produce a halt in breath. The halt in breath is a sudden disturbance of the cardiac region. It is this disturbance in the diaphragmatic and cardiac regions that is sensed as anxiety. Some people describe it as a sensation of the heart falling out, or as emptiness or cold in the region immediately below the sternum.

The vestibular branch of the eighth cranial nerve innervates the semicircular canals and the otolithic apparatus. It is
the former that senses any change in acceleration, while the
otolithic apparatus senses slow movement of the head relative
to the vertical.

Thus, the reaction that the adult interprets as fear of falling
is inherited, inborn, and needs no personal experience before
it is operative. And any sudden, sharp lowering of a newborn
infant elicits the whole series of reflexes which we regard as
the reaction to falling. The first experience of anxiety is therefore connected with a stimulation of the vestibular branch of
the eighth cranial nerve.

The foetus learns to hear in the womb where noises are not
loud but liquids transmit them better. A baby will respond
violently to very loud sudden noises, which are the only ones
by which he is affected. The stimulus is very strong, and diffusion from the hearing cochlear branch to the vestibular path
will take place. The noise must of necessity be near the thresh-
old of feeling, and is probably also sensed as pain. The baby is
startled, which also adds direct stimulation of the semicircular canals due to the jerk of the head.

The topology of the innervation of the ear is responsible for
the ready association of loud noises with fear. It also explains
why many have generally mistaken the fear of loud noises for
the first unconditioned fear. In the anthropoid and man, the
fear of loud noises is of little differential selective significance.
The newly born is so helpless that the mother carries it continuously, and had it no fear of loud noises, it would not perish
more quickly in any case. Fear of loud noises is hardly an
essential biological necessity in early infancy.

On the other hand, a newborn arboreal primate falling off
a tree, as some probably did by accident and many in violent
earthquakes, has a fair chance of survival if the thoracic cage
is made resilient by a violent contraction of the abdominal
muscles and the breath is held with the head flexed away from

the ground in the general flexor contraction. As we have said already, this not only prevents the back of the head from being smashed against the ground, but also ensures that the point of contact with the ground will be a strongly arched spine somewhere in the region of the lower thoracic vertebrae or lower, nearer the center of gravity. The shock will therefore be transformed into a tangential push along the spinal structure, on either side of the point of contact, and absorbed in the bones, ligaments, and muscles, instead of being transmitted directly to the internal organs and so injuring the body fatally. It is permissible to think that this is a selective differential factor, and that infants who did not produce such a reaction to falling had a smaller chance of reproduction. The surviving species has therefore this precise inborn reaction to falling.

It may be interesting to note that in the reaction to falling, as I describe it, support is given to Sir Arthur Keith's view that "It was on the trees, not on the ground, that man came by the initial stages of his posture and carriage."

The attitude of the body taught in Judo to break falling is exactly the same as that elicited in the baby by the stimulus of falling. Teachers of Judo and Aikido may therefore find in the above description the explanation of the difficulty of beginners to use their arms to break the fall. The arms tend to flex in accordance with the inborn reaction to falling. Beginners, therefore, tend to hurt their elbows before they learn to control and inhibit consciously the flexion of the arms. Later they learn to flap the ground, i.e. completely dissociate movement of the arms from the instinctive pattern of flexor contraction elicited by falling. Falling on the back with the head and abdominal flexors contracted enables the body to withstand a fall from a considerable height with impunity.

The baby's crying is also more understandable when it is part of the reaction to falling, rather than to loud noises. The fallen baby is in need of immediate protection and feels pain. The crying following a loud noise, would in general be superfluous, since the mother supposedly knows at least as well as the baby its significance and the information of danger it may convey.

The reflexive gripping of any object introduced into the hand of a newborn baby during the first few weeks is probably another aspect of the flexor contraction and its importance in infancy. Observing young apes clinging to the hairy chest of their mothers is strongly suggestive.

To sum up, the inborn fear is that of falling. The anatomical structure makes it imperative that the next fear that can be sensed is that of loud noises. The unconditioned sensation of anxiety is elicited by stimulation of the vestibular branch of the eighth cranial nerve. All other fears and sensations of the anxiety syndrome are therefore conditioned. The basic pattern of all fear and anxiety is the irritation of the eighth cranial nerve through at least one of its branches. The fear of loud noises is not inherited and not instinctive. In all normal infants, however, that reflex will be the first conditioned one because of the similarity of their anatomy.

Fear and anxiety are here seen to be the sensation of impulses arriving at the central nervous system from the organs and viscera. We shall see later that all emotions are connected with excitations arriving at the vegetative or autonomic nervous system or arising from the organs, muscles, etc. that it innervates. The arrival of such impulses to the higher centers of the central nervous system is sensed as emotion.

Freud's contention that anxiety is the central problem of neuroses was such that he wrote a book *Anxiety and Neuroses.* Paul Schilder finds dizziness to occupy a similar position. I quote:

Dysfunction of the vestibular apparatus is very often the expression of two conflicting psychic tendencies: dizziness occurs, therefore, in almost every neurosis. The neurosis may produce organic changes in the vestibular sphere. Dizziness is a danger signal in the sphere of the ego, and occurs when the ego cannot exercise its synthetic function in the senses, but it also occurs when conflicting motor and attitudinal impulses in connection with desires and strivings can no longer be united. Dizziness is as important from the psychoanalytic point of view as anxiety. The vestibular apparatus is an organ, the function of which is directed against the isolation of the diverse functions of the body.

It may be interesting at this point to cite Paul Schilder's following passage, reflecting an almost kindred approach to our subject:

We would expect that such a sensory organ, receiving only half-conscious impressions and leading to a motility of an instinctual and primitive type, would be very sensitive to emotions and would therefore play an important part in neuroses and psychoses. It will react strongly, and we may even expect that changes in the psyche will immediately express themselves in vestibular sensation and in tonus. Organic changes in the vestibular apparatus will be reflected in the psyche structure. They will not only influence the tone, the vegetative system, and the attitudes of the body, but they must also change our whole perceptive apparatus and even our consciousness. These general considerations make it possible that the study of the vestibular apparatus may have great importance for the understanding of psychotic and neurotic states.

Having traced the physiological source and basis of anxiety, new avenues are opened for improving, and in certain cases changing, the treatment of neuroses. Anxiety, in whatever form it may be present, must have been formed by successive conditioning from the unconditioned series of reflexes that constitute the inborn response to falling. Any treatment may therefore be considered as aiming at the extinction of a conditioned response and the formation of a more desirable one in its place. The recidive or repetitive character of anxiety may thus be explained by the indirectness and therefore often incompleteness of psychiatric treatment that leaves the somatic nervous paths untouched. The extinction of the conditioned reflexes is therefore never complete. With interruption of treatment, the muscular habitus being affected indirectly is often left unaltered. The old conditioned response will gradually be reestablished or reinforced, to put it technically.

However important this problem may be, our aim is a much wider one. We have seen that the fear of falling elicits the first inhibition of the antigravity muscles, and that anxiety is associated with this process. On examining even the most generous list of instincts, no other one but fear is found which inhibits motion. Now, the problem of "can" and "cannot" is fundamentally a question of doing, i.e. muscular activity. Even doing nothing involves muscular activity of great complexity. We may therefore expect to throw a new light on all phenomena accompanied by chronic or habitual muscular contraction. A closer study of the nervous mechanism concerned with equilibrium is therefore necessary. It is worthwhile, however, to examine more closely the ground covered, and answer some questions that arise in connection with it.

An interesting question may be asked: Why does an attacking animal roar or otherwise give up the great advantage of undetected approach to its prey? The advantage of producing a sudden loud noise is two-fold. First, sudden loud noise produced nearby elicits the response to falling, i.e. a violent contraction of the flexors, thus momentarily inhibiting the extensors. This nails the attacked animal to its place for a short instant, giving the attacker a better chance by enabling it to pounce on a fixed target instead of a fleeing one. Natural laws do not favor one species or the other, and the strong contraction of the flexors is conducive to an ulterior, much enhanced contraction of the extensors. For the longer the state of inhibition and the stronger the stretching of the extensors, the stronger will be the following outburst of contraction due to nervous induction and the stretch reflex. The attacker and the prey both derive an advantage. Normal conditions of equilibrium between the respective members of the preying species and the preyed upon are obtained by other factors. This equilibrium is, by the way, continuously shifting with a periodicity given by the climatic cycles.

The second advantage of roaring is the effect it has on the animal doing so. The expulsion of air from the lungs in roaring is conducive to vigorous diaphragmatic muscular contraction, and abates excitement. Men, too, find it easier to produce a great physical heave by an abdominal push, expelling air and producing a deep sound such as "heh" or "hah" at the same time.

That the excitation of one point of the nervous system, when strong enough or when repeated at close intervals, diffuses and radiates to neighboring centers, is a well-established fact. Darwin, in his *The Expression of the Emotions in Man and Animals,* gives a number of examples. To quote from page 80 of the "Thinker Library" edition:

As soon as some primordial form became semi-terrestrial in its habits it was liable to get dust particles into the eyes: if these were not washed out they would cause much irritation of nerve force to adjoining nerve cells, the lachrymal glands would be stimulated to secretion. As this would often recur and as nerve-force readily passes along accustomed channels, a slight irritation would ultimately suffice to cause a free secretion of tears.

As soon as by this, or by some other means, a reflex action of this nature had been established and rendered easy, other stimulants applied to the surface of the eye—such as cold wind, inflammatory action, or a blow on the eyelids—would cause a copious secretion of tears. The glands are also excited into action through the irritation of adjoining parts. Thus when the nostrils are irritated by pungent vapours, though the eyelids may be kept firmly closed, tears are copiously secreted: and this likewise follows from a blow on the nose. A stinging switch on the face produces the same effect. In these latter cases the secretion of tears is an incidental result, and of no direct service. As all these parts of the face, including the lachrymal glands, are supplied with branches of the same nerve, namely the fifth, it is intelligible that the effects of the excitement of one branch should be spread to the other branches.

The explanations of why we sneeze when looking at the sun, why we cry when we are grieved, and many other facts, are along the same lines. Translated into modern terms of conditioning of reflexes, the above quotation is very similar to the line of thought I have followed.

We have seen that in the infant, before its hearing is differentiated, i.e. before it can distinguish between different noises, only loud noises elicit a response, which is the same as to the stimulus of falling. In the adult, who has learned to inhibit this response to most loud noises of habitual occurrence, it can still be observed with unexpected very loud ones.

To quote from Starling's *Physiology:* "Auditory reflexes. . . . According to the strength of the stimulus there may be blinking of the eyes only, or, if the sound is loud, blinking and holding of breath. If stronger still, in addition to the above, all movements temporarily cease, and for a very loud sound indeed the limbs may become toneless and the body may fall."

Professor Bekessy in his classic research on hearing has shown that loud noises produce eddies in the semicircular canals in such a direction as to make the head tilt reflexively toward the source of noise. He reproduced the phenomena on his model ear.

Thus it may be considered as established that the excitation of the cochlear branch of the auditory nerve irradiates and produces a response as if the vestibular branch had been excited. Irradiations are governed by the configuration of the synapses and their valve action. It is therefore interesting to know whether excitation of the vestibular branch produces any auditory response. It seems to inhibit audition momentarily while the excitation lasts. If one falls or slips abruptly while being spoken to one has a vague impression of noise during the period while the righting reflexes operate.

We have seen that any anxiety complex established through a series of successive conditionings must have started from the inborn reactions to falling sensed through the vestibular branch of the auditory nerve. The excitation of this branch is followed by a succession of disturbances: contraction of flexors, halting of breath, accelerated pulse, sweating, blushing, and even micturition or defecation. How many of these enumerated responses will actually occur in the infant depends on the intensity, duration, and suddenness of the initial stimulus. An increased tonus of the flexors, halt of breath, and quickening of pulse accompany even the slightest excitation. Most of the time, the color of the face changes and perspiration takes place, though they may be so slight as to be perceptible only to the acute observer. The adult however, is aware of them consciously, and has in general learned to control and inhibit their completeness.

Because of habit of thought we cannot help seeing a reason and purpose in evolution as if it were the product of some intelligence like our own. In fact, we can find innumerable reasons for every reflex with every new point of view. If we examine the reflexive closing of the eyes when an intense light is thrown on them we can see the immediate effect is to shut off the intense stimulus from the retina. Next, the eyes are maintained at a level of low light intensity and the pupils accommodate by dilating so that when the eyes are reopened they are capable of distinguishing objects of normal light intensity. Without the shutting of the eyelids, the pupils would remain contracted and a longer time would elapse before the eye could see normally. In every reflex we can distinguish the same phases—the immediate reaction which undoes the effect of the stimulus or reduces it, and the after-effect which, in general, tends to eliminate the disturbance the reaction has produced in the organism, and to restore it to its original state.

The stimulus of falling similarly produces a disturbance which brings into operation all the righting reflexes. The important point to note here is that the sensation of fear and anxiety due to the disturbance of the diaphragmatic and cardiac region is actually abated by maintained general flexor contraction, and in particular that of the abdominal region. The falling body contracts its flexors to preserve the head from hitting the ground and to strengthen the spine by arching it. In the adult, the same response makes him lower his head, crouch, bend his knees, and halts his breath. His limbs are thus drawn nearer to the body in front of the soft, unprotected parts—the testicles, the throat, and the viscera. This attitude gives the best protection possible and instils a sense of safety. The flexor contractions, when maintained, are instrumental in restoring the normal, undisturbed state. The erect standing pattern is disrupted by partial inhibition of the antigravity extensors. A complete inhibition would mean falling face down. The incitations or impulses arriving at the central nervous system from the viscera and muscles in this crouched attitude evoke uteral safety, quietening of the pulse, and restoring of normal breathing. All the large articulations being flexed, the resistance to the circulation is largely increased and the pulse slowed down. The cardiac muscle must, however, be capable of the extra effort necessary to contract the heart against the suddenly increased-resistance to circulation of blood and the higher pressure in it. This was, in fact, assured by the additional adrenalin content in the blood produced by the initial fear of falling.

This pattern of flexor contraction is reinstated every time the individual reverts to passive protection of himself when lacking the means, or doubting his power, of active resistance. The extensors or antigravity muscles are perforce partially inhibited. According to my own observation, all individuals classified as introvert have some habitual reduction of their extensor tonus rigidity. Either the head or the hip joints are therefore leaning abnormally forward: turning the body is achieved by detour or roundabout means and not in the simplest direct way. Extroverts, on the other hand, have a more erect standing posture and gait.

In general, every pattern of impulses reaching the central nervous system from the viscera, muscles, and soma in general is associated with an emotional state. The muscular contraction, being voluntarily controllable, creates a feeling of power and of control over sensations and emotions. This is in fact so. To every emotional state corresponds a personal conditioned pattern of muscular contraction without which it has no existence.

Many people know that they can control in themselves physiological processes, such as preventing a headache from taking hold of them, and many other similar sensations, but dare not say so for fear of being thought ridiculous. Others, on the other hand, have elaborated this process into a theory of control of the mind over the body. All introvert and extrovert people when learning to control internal visceral functions proceed by controlling first the contraction of voluntary muscles. They form certain individual patterns which evoke the sense of well-being. This helps to prevent the reinstatement of the anxiety pattern.

We can now understand how exaggerated hyperextension of the cervical and lumbar curves becomes habitual. It is rare to see young children with the head improperly balanced. There is less voluntary interference with muscular control and the head is balanced reflexively in all alike, except for anatomical structure differences. Repeated emotional upheavals condition the child to adopt an attitude which brings a sense of safety and enables him to abate anxiety. We have seen that such passive safety is brought about by flexor contraction and extensor inhibition. Voluntary but not intended directives inhibiting the extensors are therefore observed in all emotionally disturbed persons. In the long run, this becomes habitual and remains unnoticed. The whole character is, however, affected. The partially inhibited extensors become weak, the hip joint flexes, and the head leans forward.

The pattern of reflexive erect standing is disrupted. Conflicting directives are issued from the nervous system. The lower antigravity mechanisms tend to bring the body into the normal potent state, while avoiding anxiety reinstates the crouched pattern of safety. Conscious awareness now sides with one and then with the other tendency. The antigravity mechanisms are at work without break. Like all fatigued nervous functions, they are initially overactive, hence the tonic contraction and string-like texture of the antigravity extensors. The overriding conscious control, however, prevents reflexive erect standing. Hypnotise, or otherwise relax the conscious control and erect standing at once improves to the extent the anatomical deformation of interarticulation surfaces will permit. It is essential in this context to make a clear distinction between awareness and the conscious or voluntary as opposed to the forgotten or reflexive.

People in the unfortunate situation described live on an intentional intellectual level. All their body functions are interfered with by voluntary directives. Conscious control and willpower, when properly directed, often improve certain details here and there, but intellect is no substitute for vitality. A sense of the futility of life, tiredness, and a wish to give it all up is the result of overtaxing the conscious control with the tasks the reflexive and subconscious nervous activity is better fitted to perform. Conscious control is paramount in integrating the functions fitting the mostly immediate circumstances of objective reality. The internal mechanisms enabling us to succeed should be left to the self-regulating nervous coordination. At least, in the present state of our knowledge of the nervous system, we can do no better than follow the example of the best adjusted and mature specimens, and they do not abuse the conscious control. They have a richer subjective reality.

Summary

Our internal processes, provoked by present external influences, or by forgotten, painful, previous experiences of the outside world, change our intentions to act as well as the way we act. You are as good as you wish; you are certainly more creative in imagining alternatives than you know. If you know "what" you are doing and even more important "how" you use yourself to act, you will be able to do things the way you want. I believe that the world's most important advice, "Know thyself," was first said by one who learned to know *oneself.*

A SECOND LOOK

What I have said so far only widens the field of our attention. Some would say, perhaps, that we do not "have" a skeleton, muscles, glands, nervous system, etc. They would say, and I agree, that we "are" all those things. We shall see later that semantics is not always splitting hairs. Errors often become habitual since words have multiple meanings, and the ones that last are not always what they should be.

Looking closer at what we have said, we all know that none of these parts of ourselves that I have enumerated started as we see them in the adult. In fact, they keep on changing in the adult too, but at such a slow rate that it seems not to amount to much, and therefore does not seem to matter. But the rate of change in the beginning is tremendous, the first cells doubling by division so that in nine months something like one quarter of the future adult arrives in the world. We can see that this is true when we consider the length of the baby: approximately fifty centimeters from crown to heel. In weight, a newborn is near four kilograms and this will increase about fifteen to twenty times. If we think of the rate of cell division and total numbers, we see that of the total, fifty-six of fifty-eight divisions must have occurred before the age of two. The brain in the second month of gestation is about 2.6 grams, or forty-three percent of the weight of the embryo.

In the adult, the brain weighs approximately fifteen hundred grams, but it is only about 2.4 percent of the body's total weight. By the age of two, the nervous system is about four-fifths of what it will finally become. The rate of growing slows down very rapidly from conception to early childhood. By the age of two or three, most of the functions of the nervous system are on the way to completion. Only the specifically human functions, among them movement and sex, are yet to mature. Speech, writing, mathematical skills, music, and the combination of speech and music are still developing.

When we talk about skeletons, muscles, nervous systems, and different environments we are not aware that we are thinking of the adult with all his functions grown and more or less equally mature. This concept is simply not valid and this is more important than almost anything else about humans.

It is also important to realize that people are biologically different from one another. You can transplant a piece of skin, say, from any part of an individual to any place you may like on his body. Both wounds will heal and that is all. But transplant anything from one individual to another and rejection of the transplant may kill the new bearer of the piece of someone else's body unless his own immunization is weakened artificially or the transplant is from an identical twin.

The relative sizes of the parts of the brain of one person are very different from those of any other person. Our biological makeup is as individual as our own fingerprints. To say that adults have all their functions more or less equal is very misleading; in fact, much of our common sense relies on assumptions that cannot be assumed to be legitimate and are not sensible at all. There are great similarities in men but there are individual modes of action, movement, feeling, and sensing which make each individual a unique case, and in my work he must be treated to help him in his uniqueness.

A scientist would probably say that if we wish to think properly about anything, we have to know where the thing exists—special location or a system of coordinates—and when it happens—a temporal reference system. The skeleton, the muscles, the nervous system, and the environment of the sperm and the ovum and those of the foetus six weeks old and at birth are obviously very different every instant. We are different every minute but we can select regular intervals for taking stock.

Being reasonable is also not a very good thing. I have tried to follow a reasoning that would raise no objection. However, on rereading the last few sentences I cannot help seeing through my thinking and finding in it as much reasonable nonsense as is in everybody else's reasonable nonsense. Let us look a little more critically at the last paragraph. The scientist is quite right in wishing for conditions that would make it easy to check conclusions by somebody else, somewhere else, and at another moment. But how can such a method be used on an embryo and a foetus that occur only once and where there are similarities but never identities? My growth has a lot in common with yours. We can be elements in a statistical survey, as we are not only similar enough but we are also different enough in minor details. However, there is one difference at the moment which cannot be neglected: I am writing and you are reading. There are other more important differences resulting from our environments—social, economic, racial, temporal—education, occupation, posture, interests, attitudes, and a great many other influences. In short, analysis alone is not good enough to describe the phenomenon under study. Synthesis and the history of growth must be taken into account. The analysis will be useful for marking the common features, while the whole will show how they grew to make a different human being.

A living organism is a functioning structure where, unlike man-made machines, the function makes the structure and the structure is part of the functioning. They affect each other during growth in a fashion that makes the cause and effect relationship of true or false to be a matter of opinion and little more. But, even more crucial to our thesis is that we stop and select intervals for taking stock, and thereby turn a dynamic continuously changing growing and kicking process into a series of static sequences or shots. We gradually become so absorbed in the statics of the phenomenon, which are easier to contemplate than the dynamics, that the process of growth and functioning is often so neglected as to distort the study and make it obscure. We become so uncertain that we need many subterfuges to relieve us of the anguish of doubt, insecurity, and fear.

Your brain, and mine, have a very long history. Our nervous systems are among the most complex structures in existence. They have very old layers covered by less old ones and then more recent layers. Each new layer is a formation that functions more finely. The older are primitive, and abrupt in the all-or-nothing way. Each layer checks the older ones and supercedes them. The newer the formation the finer its function. It makes action more graded, more differentiated. The older structures function more reliably faster and need less apprenticeship. The newer layers switch themselves off and allow the former more reliable swifter formation to take over and assure survival. The finer, more varied newer parts will take over once the emergency has ended. The old structures are not destroyed, they just become latent, less obvious but essential in an emergency. Any situation that cannot be dealt with at leisure will produce a regression, i.e. the older formation will take over. The newer the neural structure is, the slower it is. Gradation and variety need time and apprenticeship for deliberation and choice, following the weighing up of the pros and cons.

Slipping on a banana skin will endanger the organism if the righting of the system is not done before the fall is unavoidable. Only the old layers can deal with that effectively without thinking, hesitation, and decision, and there is no time for them. Once balance is restored we have the leisure to think, to deliberate, and may decide to clean the pavements of banana skins more often, but then there is the dilemma that if there are no banana skins to trip us, there is no righting, and no room for logical cleaning either. The old righting structures must operate in a fraction of a second, where the newer need time at their disposal. The nervous systems work in a fashion similar to our social organization. The older means of lighting, like candles or kerosene lamps or even more ancient ones, are somewhere in the house and are never used so long as there is electricity. But a prolonged blackout will produce a regression to the old candles and oil lamps.

A foetus while growing will start with the oldest formations and will proceed rapidly through the evolutionary stages, though rarely in chronological order. In the early life of a foetus, the lower jaw looks like the gills of a fish. The cerebellum has a central bundle of fibers corresponding to the horizontal position of the spine, because the movement is rotation or rolling around the spine clockwise or counter-clockwise. The newly born baby will gradually turn to roll on his stomach and return to his back. Until more recent formations in the brain and cerebellum mature and can organize this and other more complex movement, the old fish remnant will assure the fish-like horizontal rolling. In serious regression, the lying position and rolling sideways return to be the only movement available. The cerebellum will be involved in standing, posture and balance when its growth is complete. This is only an illustration of the principle and not a description of an exact process. Significantly, however, turning around the spine as an axis, i.e. turning right or left, is the most frequent movement of the body standing upright. But now the head, with all the senses that relate us to distance and space, plays a major role in turning right and left most of the time.

I first used the individual manipulative technique Functional Integration and the group technique Awareness through Movement during World War II. Already at that time I worked on one side of the body exclusively during a whole lesson. The other side remained passive or motionless all through the lesson. I wanted to create the greatest possible sensory contrast in the nervous structures and also facilitate awareness of the differences kinesthetically. I thought that the different organization of one side of the cortex and the corresponding side of the body would slowly diffuse to the other side. The person would for hours feel different mobilization and performance on his right side to that on his left side. He would thus be learning directly in his brain and from his own internal self. What would be transferred to the other side of the brain is the (learned) better patterns, by his own feeling and judgment. It was my friend, Jacob Bronowski of *The Ascent of Man* fame, who explained to me my discovery that the new side learns from the side that was involved and not the other way round. He argued that if internal feelings did not have any bias for preferring or tending to the optimal, animal life could not survive. He argued, on the same ground, that a predator moving by chance is more likely to find prey than not. If it were not so, the predator would not survive. He believed that the nervous system makes what looks to be a random act, but which is really slightly more than the fifty-fifty probability, were pure chance really involved. The same reasoning allows the prey to find water just by moving randomly. Curiously, he believed that if you feel you have to take your raincoat in the morning there is a greater probability that it will rain than that it will not.

When I began to use this one-side-only technique, I knew nothing of the recent findings about the different properties of the two hemispheres of the brain. As I often started with one side and worked another time on the other side, I discovered that some learning was easier on the right side and some on the left side. I clearly remember the moment when I realized that all the learned purely human activities, such as speaking, reading, writing, and mathematics, are predominantly the function of the left hemisphere. It is easier to attend to the details of a movement when working on the right side only (I am right-handed) and transfer this learning to the left side only mentally, in one's imagination. This, remarkably, improves the left side in about a fifth of the time. Moreover, the left side achieves greater fluency and ease than the hardworked original side. I also often start with the left side, doing the building up of the movement and the mental representation on the other. There is a difference, depending on the choice of the side, but it is not so glaring. Most students feel no difference until their sensitivity has greatly increased.

SUBJECTIVE AND OBJECTIVE REALITY

"Reality," like so many other wonderful words, was created to satisfy our constant curiosity. When we have no means to satisfy it "really," then we bunch all our kinesthetic sensations together and bring them to our consciousness by expressing them in a word. Pronouncing, or even internally feeling, seeing, or hearing the word can excite the curiosity, and also quench it in the same way as can performing a satisfactory act.

Commonly, we speak of reality, of things that are, or things that exist; they are not imagined and, therefore, may not be non-existent. As is usual with words, we have a glimpse of understanding, seeing or hearing familiar phrases and expressions, but on second thought we have doubts as to whether or not we have been correct in our understanding. Does an imaginary thing exist? What does exist mean? Do only real things exist? And if so, what is real? Is real only what we explore with our senses? I find that little effort is necessary to make any statement into something vague, unclear, or a complete tautology. The Oxford Dictionary defines "real" as "actually existing as a thing" or "occurring as a fact." Is imagination a fact, a reality? Or is imagination only supposedly an imagined fact of existence? This may seem just splitting hairs, and when I am engaged in an activity that is important to me I feel I am splitting hairs myself. However, it is a critical issue, as it concerns our knowing what we mean by knowing, what is reality, what is objective, and what is not. Above all, does it matter to me or to you, and if so in what way? The way I solve this problem to my satisfaction is to attend to what I am doing and consider the action involved. It is reduced to the essence, and what more can I find out about the movement that I call action? This kind of thing I can also feel or sense. Movement, sensing, feeling, and thinking together make me, and the thing I am dealing with, as concrete and as real as I can experience. A further concreteness that I can achieve is to find out how my ability to move, sense, feel, and think have developed with my growth to the present use I make of them. Beyond that, my thinking becomes a sensation too vague to share with anybody with whom I cannot establish a sensory contact or share my sensation.

I believe that a newborn baby has very little familiarity with the world outside himself. I say I believe, but I do not really know whether this is really so. I know, however, that I predicted, on theoretical grounds (to be scrupulous, I should say on theoretical speculation) that a newborn baby would react to sudden lowering by contracting all his flexors, halting his breath if he already has one, accelerated pulse, and getting damp if he is already dry. I said I was sure that the vestibular apparatus of the ear had evolved to the point that if babies fell, and if their falls were from trees, no baby could survive if he did not already have built into his nervous system the reaction to falling. That means that a violent stimulation of the semicircular canals of the ear would so contract the falling body that the back of the head would not hit the ground, and that the point of impact would be the arched spine somewhere near the center of gravity. The falling body may be traumatized more or less badly, but it may survive a fall of ten feet or more almost unharmed.

We see that there are things a newborn baby is familiar with; things that at first sight seem just nonsense if we are carried away by unthoughtful cerebration. We forget that the mother, and everything inside her, are subject to gravitational pull and that the baby has experienced this protected by the liquid in which he is immersed. There may even be some knowledge of a kind transmitted through the genes. Evolution has cared to bestow on other animals many such useful tricks, when their ancestors were learning and improving the means for the survival of the present generation. Man has very few helpful presents from the past which work from the start. He has, however, inherited the most useful trick of all, the ability to form his own tricks. Every individual has the ability to acquire through his experience, in his own environment, the means necessary for his successful survival.

Besides this unexpected familiarity with the outside—or is it the inside—world, the baby senses at birth touch, hot and cold, wetness and dryness, hears loud noises, and has some sort of sight, but I believe he has little or no other practical knowledge of the outside world. Every time I hear myself say something by habit such as the previous phrase, I catch myself thinking like a machine, albeit maybe a clever one.

Believe it or not, however you wish, a new baby has quite a large experience of auditory sensation. He has heard the regular beats of the heart that pumped life into him, he can tell sneezes and coughs, and he knows a great variety of gurgling noises. Scientologists and former dianeticists will tell you of other possible noises, and it should not be beyond your imagination to list more that even kings and Nobel prize winners produce. To be sure, by habit of thought and speech I have made a bad mistake; I should rather have said queens and female Nobel prize winners. Our speaking is so mechanical, or habit ridden, that if speaking means thinking, then I for one, feel ashamed for us all.

In my view, the newborn baby experiences the outside world mostly through his sensory cortex. At the very beginning he knows only a sensory subjective reality, and it is a nice reality. It goes with the sense of omnipotence, which, *nolens volens,* he will have to see shrink for the rest of his life. If he is lucky it will not become negative, but there are few who escape having at least streaks of it turned into a sense of inferiority. At the beginning, the newborn has everyone around concerned with his well-being. A cry, a movement of dissatisfaction, will mobilize everything and everybody to see that all his needs are granted.

Subjective reality is the first, the richest, and the most important to our emotional, mental, and physical well-being. It is as sound as our body and our inheritance. Gradually and surely the baby grows. His senses, which we must not forget, are not all bringing in information from outside his body. From the earliest stages he is moved by the internal needs of the entire material support of being. The nervous system, glandular balance, digestive organization, cleansing apparatus, skin, defecation, and micturition all provide an immense amount of sensory stimulation, far more than we usually care to think.

Gradually and surely the movements of the limbs and eyes become more interesting, and take up a greater part of his waking state. In the last few decades observations have been numerous and have become more reliable by cross-checking. In 1947, when I was writing *Body and Mature Behavior,* I could not find very much information on the state of the eyes of a baby at birth, at three weeks, and at other subsequent dates. Are they looking at infinity? Are their eyes capable of converging? We converge the eyes for near-seeing and set the axis of the eyeballs practically parallel for far-seeing. The reaction to falling has actually been observed a few minutes after birth, and considerable reliable knowledge has been accumulated since I first searched, relying on my curiosity and untrained amateurish observations.

It is as fascinating as any story on growth and learning to watch how a baby becomes capable of rudimentary and not quite intentional contractions of his flexor muscles, learns to roll over to one of his sides, and then onto his belly, and how the extensor back muscles become strong enough to lift his head once he is on his stomach. This lifting of the head when lying on the stomach is not like any other exercise in lifting. The head is lifted and the back muscles are contracted powerfully until the eyes are able to look forward to the would-be horizon: the head is lifted so that the face is in the position it will be when standing. Look up your family album, and maybe you will find your own photograph with head lifted much better than you hold it now.

I believe that the otolithic apparatus of the ear—tiny whiskers with little stones at their ends which produce maximum impulses when truly vertical—fixes the head so that the eyes can see the horizon most comfortably. I also believe that the turning of the baby with his head downwards takes place in sufficient time, before the head-on exit from the foetal world and entry into the baby world, for the maximum and minimum stimulation to be produced by the otolites. It is similar to balancing the indication of an electrical measuring apparatus by setting the needle exactly at zero of the scale in order to make its reading correct all along the range of measurements.

I say again (I believe this to be true but I do not really know that it is so; even so, I shall be surprised if it turns out to be just a nice speculation), I have during forty years or so observed many people with bad posture, which as you know already means to me also insufficiently organized intentional movements, and have often found that the "otolithic standardization period" was much shortened by circumstances.

Step-by-step subjective reality will give way to a slowly growing complex of sensations of a special kind—sensations which surrounding people approve or condemn. Parents, teachers, visitors, will either say, "Nice boy," (or girl), or with the appropriate grimace, "Ugh, don't do that." By and by, it will dawn on the new apprentice to adulthood that some of his most cherished subjective reality is not acceptable to those who provide his needs and above all the security of forthcoming care and affection. Gradually, he will learn that only a small part of his subjective reality is shared by others, or rather, the baby will become aware only of that part endorsed by others. It is easier to become aware of each disapproval as it happens than it is to be aware, stage by stage, of the totality of the reduced internal life.

Omnipotence, which is lived and not perceived, is eroded in quite an incomprehensible way. A baby having fun standing on a chair, holding its back, and rocking to and fro will be precipitated upon by a parent with an expression of danger and concern. They will grab the child with unaccustomed intensity and in a most authoritive way prohibit such a thing, while in fact, few babies injure themselves this way. The innate fear of falling will either inhibit the amplitude of oscillations, or the baby will slip off in time to get away with only a fright or minor contusion. However, the onlooker cannot afford to watch an act that might finish with banging the back of the head on a stone floor, especially when the possibility of severe injury with internal bleeding cannot be excluded. Even so, we are not concerned at this moment with the methods of educating children, we are instead concerned with objective reality. Objective reality grows slowly, eroding subjective reality, and alongside this process, the curiosity to try anything once to see what happens, which we interpret as omnipotence, is diminished at the same time.

From this point of view, all acts and notions which in the end we find in all the adults around us will constitute the objective reality of us all. Objective reality is thus, of necessity, part of all the subjective reality which grows unhindered and without interference, simply and luckily because parents do not know "how". Subjective reality is as sound as our biological makeup. Objective reality shows our growth as a member of human society, as part of a culture or even a civilization.

Our objective reality, reflected by our behavior in our social environment, is a measure of our sanity. Suppose I say that I like or detest Bach's music. People, if they are not pop mad, may think that I have very good musical taste or that I am not musical at all, as the case may be. I, and my judges, deal with taste which is a subjective affair; it is private business and nothing more or less. An old Hebrew saying has it that there is no point in arguing about taste or smell. Suppose, on the other hand, that I seriously maintain that I am Bach—it is more usually Napolean and occasionally Jesus Christ—and I ask you to treat me as such, then if I behave this way continuously and unintentionally for a long enough period, I will be locked up. Tacitly agreed objective reality is a measure of your sanity and mine. If we infringe, contradict, or sin against the reality that life in a society has annexed from our subjective life, then our sanity as a member of that society will be doubted. One can glimpse here an effective method of dealing with socially rejected individuals. An effective method is not seen in any way clearly at the moment. On introspection we can usually find in ourselves streaks of behavior which we suppress for fear that we may be judged insane, for to most people, even now, insanity exists only as a disease or defect of the brain.

I have repeatedly said that objective reality is only a part of subjective reality. It took me a long time and much labor to arrive at this conclusion and to see also the utility of such a conclusion. For lack of an easier way out we rely on evolution as the most proven and accepted method of seeing life, and ourselves, in true perspective in the general scheme of the universe. We have, at present, no better approach and no better way of seeing life in the general scheme of things than the theory of evolution. There are old adversaries of the theory who, from time to time, consider that they have found new flaws in it, but on the whole, the theory has been improved and is generally accepted as reliable.

What I have said above about subjective and objective realities is not easy to digest. I have repeatedly reconsidered the question. The evolution of the nervous system in all mammals shows that the subjective world of reality is very much larger than the objective one. This is clearly seen in the structure of the nervous system.

The number of nerve cells is usually taken to be $3 \cdot 10^{10}$ We know objective reality through our senses: hearing, seeing, smelling, tasting, touching, cold and hot, wet and dry. The number of neurons that inform us of the outside environment —which we, in short, glibly consider as reality—should be, one would think, enormous compared with the total number of them in the entire system. It turns out that in the basilar membrane there are about ten thousand nerve cells, making twenty thousand for the two ears. There are, of course, many other cells in the ear, but it is a question whether they are part of the inner activity, or only analyze audible information from outside. So, let us say fifty thousand cells, to be on the safe side. The retina is supposed to have one hundred and fifty thousand cones, rods, and whatever you like, which for the two eyes makes three hundred thousand. Our nose comes out very poorly, but our tongue is richly innervated on the tip and edges; estimate however you may, fifty thousand is a good guess for the two of them. So far as our body is concerned, the tips of our fingers are generously innervated, but the lower back has a nerve ending only every four to five centimeters. Consider our body surface as one thousand square centimeters, with an average density of innervation of ten each square centimeter, we then arrive at ten thousand, which we can take to be twenty-five thousand just because I am not too particular. Summing up, at this point, we have a grand total of six hundred twenty-five thousand. I will agree to a safety factor to make it three million or even $30 \cdot 10^6$ which is an exaggeration. So that out of $3 \cdot 10^{10}$ cells only $3 \cdot 10^7$ at the very most can be informing our interior of the world outside us, which is less than one cell for every thousand cells that manipulate, analyze, and integrate data or whatever it is that the nervous system does. You may find it easier to agree with me that only one cell in ten thousand is bringing in information from objective reality, and that subjective reality is immensely richer and more complex.

We can easily imagine our earth without living matter at all. In fact, we know that the earth had no oxygen in the atmosphere at one time, and that radiation even more obnoxious to live with than the X-rays we use today did not follow life into existence. It was only when, by a series of accidents or somebody's mistake, we had an atmosphere capable of filtering out the obnoxious radiation, mostly by absorption and otherwise, that life became possible on earth. In other words, there is a Reality which has given birth to the subjective mother reality—nine months—and the objective father reality—a few minutes.

This cosmic Reality is so immense and overwhelming that it is only when we are at our best that we can catch glimpses of it. We have to be a poet, a mathematician, a musician, and a philosopher to have any idea of the immensity, extent, matter, energy, or duration, all of which are beyond our imagination, let alone grasp. Our knowledge, which was acquired by so much exertion on the part of the best human brains, is only a measure of our ignorance of this Reality, and a challenge to our future.

Summary

I believe the future of man is better and more interesting than anything even science, the most vigorous human tool, has provided and may make us believe. Today, "reality" is only the sum total of external and internal processes that we do not suspect to be alterable by us.

AWARENESS
THROUGH
MOVEMENT

There is an old, Chinese saying: "I hear and forget. I see and remember. I do and understand."

Like all sayings, it is not quite right but it contains wisdom. We do not forget everything we hear and we do not remember everything we see. I do believe, however, that we understand best what we can do. But I have "blocks," "phobias," "ties," "inhibitions," and "compulsions" that limit my doing to repetitive patterns with no other choice, no way out. My understanding relates to things I can do. I cannot, for the love of Mike, understand why I feel impotent; I cannot understand why I am depressed; I cannot understand why, today, I am so virile and gay. So, even to do does not make for absolute understanding. Then what does? Resolve the "absolute" and you may have better understanding.

When I began to work on myself, or more correctly with myself, because of my trouble with my knees, I did not distinguish between manipulative Functional Integration and group work to produce Awareness through Movement. I used them indiscriminately as I did not realize that there was a difference. Gradually, however, I came to see that what I was doing with myself was not simple, and certainly not easy, to communicate to others. I had no intention of doing that, but it happened that a colleague, a physicist, asked to participate in what I was doing with myself. Thus I had to share my experience with somebody. Imitating me did not satisfy him as he did not know how or where to look, and he was also unable to discern what was essential and what was a mere detail. The more questions he asked the more I disliked his presence; I was irritated by my inability to explain in a few words exactly what I was doing. I found I had to go back into my past to find my way of self-direction, the reasoning, and later the feeling, that moved me to do what I did. I was jealous of the waste of time and annoyed with myself; I disliked his inquisitiveness, and my own feeling of impotence made him a nuisance.

As my work with myself seemed to me self-observation, it occurred to me that self-examination involves judgment, good or bad. My annoyance was that I had to examine myself, whereas when I had been alone I was able just to observe myself as an object which acted and moved. I was far more absorbed in observing how I was doing a movement than I was interested in what that movement happened to be. This seemed to me the real gist of my knee trouble. I could repeat a movement with my leg hundreds of times, I could walk for weeks with no inconvenience whatsoever and suddenly doing what I believed to be the identical movement just once more spoiled everything. Obviously, this one movement was done differently from the former ones, and so it seemed to me that how I did a movement was much more important than what the movement consisted of.

Having someone share the feeling of what I did with myself is like throwing a stone and disturbing the quiet surface of a pool of water. To come to the point, it became clear to me that I was dealing with a process of self-direction and each particular movement was important only inasmuch as it illuminated this process. As the process was obviously not perfect in my case, it seemed that it might also be imperfect in other people. As faulty heredity did not have to be considered, there having been no trouble with my knees for a decade or two, it remained only to discover how I came about learning the process of self-direction the way I did. No baby is born with the ability to perform adult movements; they have to be learned while growing. I had, therefore, to relearn as an adult that which I had failed to learn better in my past. Learning to learn was the thing I had to share with my colleague. I was not a teacher, yet he had to learn how I did whatever it was he saw me doing.

I began by making him realize that learning is very different from doing. In life an act must be accomplished at the right speed, at the right moment, and with the right vigor. Failure in any of these conditions will compromise the act and make it fail. The act will not achieve its purpose. Achieving the intended purpose may be considered as a condition in itself. The intended purpose may be just moving for the sake of moving or dancing for the sake of dancing. Yet, all these conditions for successful achievement in life are a hindrance in learning. These conditions are not operative during the first two or three years of life when the foundations for learning are dug and laid.

For successful learning we must proceed at our own rate. Babies repeat each novel action clumsily at their own rate until they have enough of it. This occurs when the intention and its performance are executed so that they are just one act which feels like an intention only.

An adult learning to play tennis or golf or anything else repeats until he feels that his achievement should be approved by others or that he evokes the approval by actually winning. A baby cannot do otherwise, and an adult does not know what his rate of learning is. His appreciation is distorted by what he happened to impose on himself as the rate of a "normal" person. During his life as a child, at home and at school, with other siblings or children, the parents and the teachers all tried to push him to be exactly like they were, with a rate of learning which was not his own and which he will strive probably all his life to achieve.

In learning Awareness through Movement, proceed very slowly, so slowly that you can discover your rate of learning here, when the demands of your ambition and the rate of others do not make you go faster than you can. In Awareness through Movement lessons everybody is allowed all the time necessary to assimilate the idea of the movement and the leisure to get used to the novelty of the situation. There is sufficient time to perceive and organize oneself, and to repeat the movement as often as one feels is right. No whistle, no metronome, no rhythm is used, no music and no drum. You slowly learn to find your innate rhythm, depending on your structure. Each member of the body has its rate of oscillation, like a pendulum. With growing familiarity of the act, speed of movement increases and consequently its power. This may not be self-evident but it is correct. The slowness is necessary for the discovery of parasitic superfluous exertion and its partial elimination. The superfluous in action is worse than the insufficient, for it costs us useless effort. Fast action when learning is strenuous, leads to confusion, and makes the learning unpleasant and unnecessarily tiring.

Learning must be pleasurable, and it must be easy; the two make breathing simple. What is learnt otherwise rarely becomes habitually spontaneous. In Awareness through Movement lessons you make the impossible possible, then easy, comfortable, pleasurable, and finally aesthetically pleasing. I believe it is more important to learn the way to learn new skills than the feat of the skills themselves; the new skill is only a useful reward for your attention. You will feel you deserve the skill and this will help to build your self-confidence.

In order to arrive at the right movement, it is first necessary to think of better movement rather than right; the right movement has no future development. For several Olympiads, jumping two meters four centimeters was the right thing for a gold-medalist to do, and so long as this was considered right even such a superb athlete as Owens could not do better. Today one needs to go over two meters twenty centimeters to qualify for competion, and many jump two meters thirty centimeters. The better can be improved—the right remains the limit for ever. Think of such great runners as Nourmi and Ladoumeque, they would not qualify today even for the semifinals. Better can be bettered—right and correct remain forever right and correct and deflate one. This is not just playing with words, as we usually do with words: imagine your attitude of mind when you feel that you have not achieved your best but feel you could have made a little greater effort; compare this with your state of mind when, after a supreme effort, you do not attain your goal and so feel discouraged and diminished in your own eyes. In the first case there is the urge to repeat, not so in the second.

In Awareness through Movement lessons I start with the constituents of the movement, and sometimes there may be as many as twenty different variations of the constituent partial configurations of the final skill. The preliminary ingredient movements do not usually evoke the final act. In this manner everybody is at ease and not urged to go all out to achieve. This is contrary to the prevailing methods of education in which we are often wired in to strive for success and achievement, in spite of our better judgment. By shifting our attention to the means of achieving instead of the urge to succeed, the learning process is easier, quieter, and faster. Striving for a goal reduces the incentive to learn, but by adopting a level of action well within our means we can improve our way of acting and reach much higher levels in the end.

When learning, do not have any intention of being correct; do not act well or nicely, do not hurry, as this creates confusion; instead go slowly and use no more, but rather less, strength than you need. Do not concentrate, for this means literally not looking around. Concentration is a useful principle sometimes in life, but in learning, attention must be directed alternately to the background and the figure. In learning, you have to know first the trees and then the forest where they belong. The shifting from figure to background and vice versa becomes so familiar that one can simultaneously perceive both, without any bothering or striving to be efficient. Elimination of useless parasitic action will make for efficiency surer than just striving for it. Do not be serious, eager, avoiding any wrong move. The kind of learning that goes with Awareness through Movement is a source of pleasurable sensations which lose their clarity if anything dims the pleasure of it all.

Errors cannot be avoided in learning even if we rely solely on strict imitation; learning to us means grasping the unknown. Any act may lead to the unknown. If you eliminate what seems erroneous at the start you may make the learning void of any interest altogether. Errors can be eliminated when we know what is right, but when we know what is right we can do without further learning; simple repetition or exercising will teach us a sort of achievement. Awareness through Movement leads to knowledge of oneself and to previous undiscovered resources in oneself. So, do not avoid errors, but rather use them as alternatives for what you feel is right and their roles may soon be interchanged.

I use the word "awareness" as conscious knowledge, and it is not to be mixed up with simple consciousness. I am quite familiar with my house and my library, but I am not aware of how many steps I have to climb to get home. I am conscious of leaving and returning home all through the years, yet I am not aware of the number of steps on the stairs. If I pay attention once and count the number of acts, such as shifting the eyes and performing whatever movements may accompany them in my head, arms, and legs, then I become aware that before I was only consciously mounting the stairs. Once I am conscious of how I am shifting my attention from one step to the other I am aware of them and I also know their number.

The same train of thought could apply to my library. "Awareness" is used by me to denote conscious-of plus knowledge. I am conscious that I can swallow intentionally for nearly a whole lifetime without being aware of how I do it. Nobody is aware of how we do it.

Speaking of awareness, I have found that even students of mine make the mistake of thinking that I recommend them to be aware of all their actions all the time they are awake. My learning is enhanced by becoming aware that to lift my right foot off the ground I have to mobilize preliminarily my right hip joint which means I have to shift most of my weight to the left, if only for a wink. Once I have learned this new style of walking it becomes semi-automatic; even so my awareness is now triggered into control at the slightest disturbance of the excellency of my walking. In my own case, I have managed to do practically anything with myself with two defective knees, and this is only because I am aware of what I am going to do, and how I am going to do it before I make an irreparable and defective movement. But most of the time, in normal conditions, I walk with simple intentional walking as I did before I became aware of how to walk with defective knees. I do not count the steps of my house every time I mount them, and I can allow myself this luxury only because of the liberty my awareness gives me.

Procedures similar to Awareness through Movement can be detected in learning to paint, to play an instrument, or solve a mathematical problem. A painter in front of an easel with pencil, charcoal, or brush in hand, looks at the face or figure before him which he has to reproduce on the paper or canvas on his easel. He looks at the face and at the paper, he weighs his hand, he frees it from power, and this enables him to feel certain that he can draw what he sees. In order, however, to reproduce what is in front of him he has to look at it again and again until he is fully aware of what he sees. Is it an oval face? Are the eyes near the outline of the face or are they more central? And so on. When he learns Awareness through Movement he can appreciate and detect whether he draws or paints better and more fluently when he is breathing in, breathing out, or just holding his breath. This awareness through or while moving will, in the end, produce a painter who seems able to look and draw naturally without any effort. The time spent on self-observation in action—which is movement—is insignificant when compared with the readiness of the resulting excellence and fluency.

A violinist, an actor, a writer, or whoever, who is not aware of the importance of awareness of the way one directs oneself in acting or functioning in life will stop growing the moment he achieves what he considers to be the right way of doing. Some pianists of genius when practicing are always aware of their playing and discover an alternative to the habitual. Improvement of talented people comes through their awareness of themselves in action. Their talent arises from their freedom to choose their modes of action. New modes of action are available to those who have discovered themselves, or who have had the good luck to meet a teacher who helped them to learn to learn. Such teachers teach music and not the this and that of any particular score. The same goes for all human skills and art. The most common feature of people who achieve indescribable and superb performance is the hours of daily practice they all undertake throughout their lives. Hours of repetitive practice is hard work; hours of practicing awareness in movement or action remain the most absorbing and interesting time in our lives. The feeling of being alive relates to the awareness of growing to be oneself.

It was my good fortune to witness an instance of awareness of what we hear. I was leaving the laboratory after the installation of a newly designed Curie balance following the discarding of one which had served several decades. Frederic Joliot-Curie, on our way home, called me to see the new instrument of which he was very proud. The instrument had fifteen hundred volts between the central suspension and the housing which was earthed. It was late and every one else had left the laboratory except us. Joliot took another last look, removed his overcoat, and indulged in trying out the instrument. He put a metal strip, which had been left near the instrument, in the chamber and switched on the counter, when there was a stream of clicks in the loudspeaker. Joliot expressed his ire that the notice he had had put up requesting that the last person to leave the laboratory should switch off the instrument had not been obeyed. He put on his coat and we were leaving for home when, reaching for the switch, he stopped as if struck by lightning. Whereupon he took off his coat once more and stood by the balance oblivious of everything else. Listening to the clicking he turned and said, "Can you not hear the dying-out clicking? There is no radioactive material here which has such a half-lifetime." Once he had switched off the machine as he had instructed we left for home. Next day there was the news that induced radioactivity had been discovered. Had he not become aware of the noises he had heard there would probably have been just a dressing down for the person who had left the machine "not switched off". It took Joliot nearly a week to make sure, to convince himself and then the world that induced or artificial radioactivity is indeed an experimental fact. He was rewarded by a Nobel prize. I believe that not very many physicists have the awareness available to Frederick Juliot-Curie and that many would just have thought something was wrong with the new machine.

People often explain away incidents like this as intuitive. To me it is a matter of semantics. Intuition works in the field in which the person has both wide experience and a vital personal interest. The sound of sea waves are heard by many, but only Debussy had an intuitive musical theme for his *La Mer*. Debussy hearing what Joliot heard would, we hope, have had another musical inspiration. Saying that Joliot became aware of what he was hearing seems to me to be a clearer statement, which is more precise both fundamentally and generally. Intuition is an acceptable explanation, but with the reservation that it can apply only to men in the domain in which their entire personality has an intense interest. We have the choice to think whatever we wish. We do, in fact, have alternatives; I choose awareness.

In the four decades of my involvement with human learning I have become aware of the difficulty which even interested and intelligent students have in understanding how it is that I am able to improvise, year in and year out, thousands of movements each with ten or more variations on the same theme until even the slowest in the audience receives the message. The usual explanations people offer me are that I am unique, and that I have creative ability to an uncommon degree. I am deliberately omitting other complimentary sayings and writings, not from modesty but because I see nothing to be proud of. I once heard a saying that struck me; it was that the average man in the street is you and I. I believe that the average latent genius is you and I. Without the inner conviction of offering to my listeners and readers something important to every human being I could not have had the stamina to persist alone for decades. During a lengthy and instructive conversation which I was privileged to have with Jonas Salk in the Salk Institute in San Diego he exclaimed, "People like you and me are alone in the world—we should keep together." This is not true for we are not alone most of the time but we feel so at low ebb.

I believe that the latent abilities in every one of us are considerably greater than the ones we live with. Moreover, the latency is actively imposed by ourselves because of lack of awareness. I believe that the miseries of life of men since the dawn of known history, ten or twelve thousand years in all, have been so great that our present state is not a failure but just a fact. The immense speculative possibilities opened to humans with the explosive thinking spreading from one discipline to the other present us with the following few issues. We shall find ourselves so at fault with our present brain that we shall have to substitute for it the computers of the future or we shall see an increased evolution in our present ability. I, personally, believe that the prospects for our future are already becoming available. I believe that we already possess a brain which occassionally functions at full capacity, provided we become aware of how we avoid using it. Our present cultural programming of most brains is habitual in content, intention, and scope. We limit our growth to what is immediately useful, just as we always have. We are wasting our abilities by using only those that we need in our condition of misery which we ourselves have created. Just think of the speed of reading which is an immense achievement, but is it really necessary to read at the rate of speaking (three hundred words a minute at its best)? Is it at that rate because we learn to read and write with the help of speech, and so have to continue forever in the same way? We soon kid ourselves that the achieved rate of reading is the limit of our brain. This is when you certainly know that by learning to scan the written or typed script with the eyes and the head only, which is divorcing conceiving the content from subvocal speaking or by inhibiting subliminal utterings, we can read ten times as fast. Moreover, when reading at three thousand words a minute, we improve our retention of the content and its details. Are you sure that we cannot multiply by ten most of our abilities which we have inadvertently limited by some other "useful" criteria, as we have done with speech and writing?

I believe that we actually limit ourselves by an undue and erroneous emphasis on *what* is important to the society of men at the neglect of *how*. How each individual can be helped to find his uniqueness and become unique in his contribution to himself and his social environment is too often neglected. There are many Leonardo da Vincis in the human species, yet we do everything that makes full human capacity a rarity.

Our own generation can list musical, mathematical, electronical, and computorial interspatial uniqueness, exhibiting latent, never used abilities of deduction and induction, of carrying pattern recognition from one mental discipline to the other. There are similar discrete jumps in athletics as well. All brain activity flourishes with the familiarity of the domain it dwells on. Operational calculus, large systems, modern genetics, tensor calculus, cybernetics are not extensions of known beginnings enlarged. They are new patterns of thinking that can be detected as latent abilities hampered and made inoperative through scientific ignorance. Education of the young, I hope soon to be able to say, was generally a striving for the smallest common denominator of uniformity. The few geniuses in each generation had their individuality fostered through luck. Here and there was somebody who taught them to learn rather than only teaching a curriculum, no matter how good.

I have formed in my imagination an ideal human brain and function. Ideal means non-existent. It also means that everybody may have one or more streaks approaching comparison with the ideal. It is a very useful auxiliary to compare everyone to the ideal. What is that ideal being? It is a normal or average person who has an average genetic inheritance, who had ideal birth, babyhood, childhood, and growth to adulthood. What sort of conditions are necessary to grow such a monster? I have great difficulty in starting; had there been anywhere an ideal human it would not be so presumptuous to clarify an ideal history of growth. To think it is not so difficult as to describe it in words. When I do not have to account for the logic of saying my thinking I am at liberty to ascribe ideal qualities to each structure and its function. Each function is much easier to idealize. An ideal memory is, of course, a memory which has ideal retention, has ideal recall, and remains absolutely under intentional control. Idealized antigravity function of the skeleton and its musculature means levitation-like lightness at will in all directions and at any moment.

Observe that this way of thinking of such an ideal set-up does not present much difficulty, as the mind does not have to worry about it.

In this manner you may form for yourself an ideal image of the ideal function of an ideal man. The advantage of such a subterfuge is very considerable, for at a glance you can place "function" of the real man in comparison with the image in your mind and obtain very useful concrete information. I have examined Olympic gold-medalists and found that some jump struggling against gravitation as if levitation never existed whereas others seem light enough and jump even higher with less effort, so much so that you could imagine they feel weightless. All may even jump the same height but how they did it becomes of first importance. One may even be only a silver-medalist but still nearer to ideal levitation than any of the others.

Watching the same person perform several acts I can see him, or her, bending to sit on the floor, waltzing with somebody, and being asked to say something before an audience. I find that this person's waltzing looks more like my ideal image than the other acts, and I wonder how this far from ideal posture manages to waltz so nicely. Then I observe that most of the turning couples do better than during other actions, and that something in the waltzing has brought lightness to otherwise heavy, clumsy individuals. In most people there is more lightness in rotary movement around oneself than in other movements. Without my ideal image I am at a loss to know what to look for; each function grades itself when compared with an idealized function, and although this is not a measure (as from a scientific instrument) it is still a mental auxiliary of the greatest value to me. It has guided my inquiry in neurology, physiology, evolution theory, and so forth, enabling me to find the pertinent facts which are dispersed in an ocean of knowledge and intelligence which in itself has no ports, only vistas.

Man's ideal posture is one of the features that I have considered most over the years so that I have arrived at a precise idea—or ideal—reinforced by scientific findings and by long practice. Today, I often start a workshop with an experiment clarifying to the audience the intricate and intrinsic beauty of upright standing in man.

Here is how many thousands have been introduced to the practice of Awareness through Movement. Look at the illustration which shows how a baby just before beginning to crawl, and in its early stages, holds his head while lying on his stomach.

The head is held reflexively just as it would be in the ideal head of an ideal adult. The head is lifted until the eyes look at the horizon, and held freely so it can move right and left with the greatest smoothness and ease the human nervous system can muster. The rest of the body contorts itself so that the cervical spine is in a position to allow freedom of the head to move on the atlas and axis vertebrae. On watching a baby, long before it is a year old, turning or being turned on its stomach, one can see the head orienting itself as if by an invisible mechanism to the position shown in the illustration. The holding of the head is indefatigable as well as reflexive, and it can remain there to outlast a strong adult, always assuming he can reproduce it. A baby may lower its head every now and then giving the impression that its nose will strike the ground, but this does not happen; the head rights itself in the nick of time as if a switch were turned on.

In the adult, the head turns intentionally and also automatically in reaction to any sudden changes in the teleceptors' stimulation. In either case, or for whatever other "factor", the head turns right or left to locate the source of the change. The head is twisted until the organs of sight, hearing, and smell are equally stimulated, and in the long run even the shortest changes will turn the head to the source. The nervous system has learned to orient the head to the source by the difference in the stimulation of these organs, as well as by their equality when the duration of the change is sufficient. The important thing is that the rotation of the head to face the source of the change organizes the entire musculature to move the skeleton so that the brunt of the weight of the body is carried by the leg of the side to which the head is turned.

Try to imagine something sudden, important, or dangerous happening on your right side and simulate the movement of your head in such an occurrence. You will realize that your left side is freed from weight carrying so that you can, or actually turn your body to the right. The right side is toneful enough to free the body to turn around the right hip joint, the leg, or the foot, or all of them, to face the disturbance. The immense nervous activity necessary to redistribute the tonus of the entire musculature from one pattern to another is achieved in a wink. It is triggered by the asymmetrical tension in the muscles of the neck that control the head. It is important to understand the mechanism of the movement of the eyes as well as the effect of the cochlear stimulation in the process. But I cannot indulge in recounting the details that can be found initially in the work of Magnus and now in almost every good treatise of modern physiology. The final result of facing the disturbance of the rotation of the body is to turn it as if the object is to restore the symmetry of the muscles of the head and eyes. This is achieved with such great economy in organization and action that the response to danger or vital interests is practically instantaneous. Rotation is so well developed in humans that they turn faster than most animals, and in bull-fighting, Japanese martial arts, boxing, and all such activities, impact with an oncoming object or thrust can be avoided by simply turning sideways. The system is so well structured and so fast most of the time that self-preservation seems miraculous.

The dynamics of moving solids require that the energy be proportional to the square of the velocity, leading one, maybe, to expect that fast rotation requires tremendous effort. This is not so, for in our upright posture the proximity of the weighty matter to the axis of rotation reduces the effort to a minimum. Also our bodies are almost ideally cylindrical, making the moment of rotation as small as possible. In Awareness through Movement a series of fast movements is practiced which gives rise to an exhilarating sense of being lighter and faster than we can believe.

When you remember all my reasons, do's and don'ts regarding learning, you will understand why, in the examples I am about to give you, I do not wish you to read ahead. It will be much better for you if you work slowly step by step and arrive at the final version your own way. It will then be not my way of doing, but your own way, which is as it should be.

Sit on the floor. Put your hands behind you and lean on them with your arms almost straight at the elbows. Bend your knees so that you can put the soles of your feet flat on the floor in front of you. Tilt both knees to your right using your feet as hinges for moving your legs and knees. Tilt your knees to the left and back to the right. While repeating these tiltings of the knees right and left observe that the knee movement is initiated by your pelvis. Note that tilting your knees to the right is preceded by the stiffening of the left arm so that the push of the left hand on the floor facilitates the initiation of the movement of the pelvis, coinciding with lifting and tilting your head slightly backwards. Repeat your knee tiltings right and left while attending to the preliminary alteration of your trunk, spine, and head, and to your exertion. Go slowly and you will find each time easier until you are aware of exactly when you breathe in and when you breathe out during the phases of the movement. Change to breathing out at the moment when, in the first instance, you were breathing in and continue until you become aware which makes the tilting easier. Whether your decision is right or wrong is immaterial at this point. *For, when your attention and awareness are improved, in a few moments, your judgment will be better, as your sensitivity will increase with the reduction of your efforts.* The situation proposed is realizable by either sex, fat or emaciated, old or young, atheletes as well as the not too severely crippled. Keep tilting your knees for a minute or two, or for a dozen times, or for however long you feel comfortable.

The difference between one person and another will be slight and consist mostly in how many rehearsals are necessary for one to become aware of the part the rest of the body has to play in making the intention easily realizable. Becoming aware is the significant part of your learning, and it is not at all important which movement is used for the lesson; even so we might just as well choose one which is also useful in life. You will, in the end agree, that you, as a human being, can move like a cat and about ten times as fast as what you have, up to now, accepted as your "normal". Remember the rate of reading, and my contention that normal is the potentially possible, deformed and limited to "normality". The point is so important that it is worth repeating. Except for parts of ourselves, everyone of us uses only a small fraction of our latent ability. The habit of thinking that one must have talent, or be born with it, in order to be good at anything at all, is as true as it is an obstacle to free choice. It is, however, true that we are genetically human, and that what other humans can do, even if it is only one, all the others can. Take the example of speech, and the three thousand different ways of achieving it. Mouth cavities, teeth, tongues, and brains are as widely different as abilities. The refusal to allow oneself the status of not being talented as in the use of languages is part of the mental laziness which is the ill-health of most humans. It is very hard to work to be a genius musician, painter, mathematician, actor, or whatever so as to create an original article or object, so personal that it bears the hallmark of its maker. It is far easier to be one of the multitude which our education renders as uniform as it can be.

By this time you will have rested and become aware of many things you may or may not have known. Sit again in the position to tilt your knees right and left. This time tilt with your knees spread a little apart, until there is room for first one of your legs and feet to lie on the floor between your knees and then the other. Thus, when your knees are on the floor tilted to the right, your right lower leg can lie freely between them with the sole of the foot resting squarely against the left thigh near the knee; of course your left leg and foot are also on the floor. Observe that to achieve this your feet are used as hinges for the tilting legs, and remain practically on the floor at the location that they have found for themselves while you were tilting and spreading your knees. Using the feet as hinges is crucial throughout to the end of the final phases of the movement.

Familiarize yourself with the details of the preparations necessary to make the two symmetrical positions of yourself when the knees are tilted to the right and then to the left. Breathe easily, which means do nothing to breathe other than watching to see that there is no breach of continuity of air coming in or out of your nostrils. Find out which hand on the floor becomes useless when you tilt your knees to your right; one can be lifted without making anything more difficult or causing a halt in breathing. Tilt your knees to your left and back to your right; this time lifting the other hand off the floor. You will then become aware of what you have just read or understood.

Keep on tilting your knees right and left. Lift the hand that you found unnecessary to lean on and carry it in the direction of your knees. Gradually you will find it more and more comfortable to lift the pelvis sufficiently to stand on your knee. Sit, tilt your knees to the other direction until you stand on your other knee again. Sit and rehearse these movements several times. Note that the feet serve as hinges and otherwise do little to assist in the movements and are better left alone to move as they will. You should, however, become aware and watch that they are not displaced without your intention. The lifted arm is carried with the trunk, and you can swing it lightly to assist the trunk and pelvis in being lifted off the floor.

I make such remarks only after I see that the students have already realized and are already doing what I am verbalizing. In this way the student feels he has guessed correctly and his reliance and confidence grow with his awareness. In written descriptions like this much of the highlighting is, of necessity, blurred, the timing of the remarks being dictated by the paper.

You are encouraged to rest as soon as you feel tired and to start again when you are ready. So start again with what you were doing. Turn to your left until you are on your knee, with your right arm flung forward to your left; you are still leaning on your left arm with its hand on the floor. To get up on our feet from this position we usually put the right foot forward on the floor and heave ourselves upright by a concentrated effort of both legs. This immobilizes the moving body, annihilates the kinetic impetus, and makes the getting up slow and laborious. It is the equivalent to putting on the brakes of a car going uphill after it has gathered momentum, when the only choice is to return to the lowest gear, start the ascent again (wasting petrol), and wait for sufficient kinetic energy for higher gears to be used. In the movement that we are learning now we are not yet as clearly aware of bad driving. Start again, tilt your knees to your right, swing them to the left, but this time swing the right arm in front of you upward to your left and continue the pelvic movement in its spiral ascent from the floor until it raises the right hip joint sufficiently (in the direction of your moving right arm) to straighten the right knee. Your right foot will stand on the floor. As the pelvis carries both hip joints, the left one will also rise enough for you to feel yourself standing on both feet with your entire weight. The pelvis moves from the sitting position and twists spirally upward to your left, and if you are sufficiently aware of the trajectory of the pelvis, and do not stop it but let it follow its course, it will complete its rotation until you are facing what was your rear standing on your feet. In this movement you are using the original impetus of your pelvis and trunk, which helped to swing your knees to the left. Start again until you are aware of how you direct yourself while moving. Getting up, starting from sitting with both knees to your right and swinging leftwards to stand facing backwards will be practically instantaneous and effortless. Repeat, starting with your knees tilted to the right and attend to the uninterrupted motion of the pelvis. Your arms, feet, and everything else will then organize themselves perfectly with the pelvis. This is because the head is carried in the same ascending spiral, with the eyes moving to find the horizon when the ascent is completed.

Sit on the floor, close your eyes and see with your mind's eye the trajectory of your head and pelvis. When you are clearly aware of the movement, then think of the ease and speed with which you rose from sitting to standing in one simple action.

This apparent simplicity is due to the integration of all the complexity of details into one act of intention. Repeat again, starting with the knees tilted to your right as before, but this time do not lift your left hand decisively after all your weight is on your feet, which means you do not complete the movement to be fully upright. Stay in this position and imagine how to return to the initial sitting configuration. You may take as long as it is necessary for you to become aware of your displacement in space. This spatial awareness is but another facet of your kinesthetic sensation. In well learned intentional movement, attention glides so easily from internal contact of muscular sensation to spatial or external contact that we do not feel we are doing it. A single act is simple even if it is as complex as writing this description.

You have probably found that to reverse a movement in space, it is also reversed in its timing. We cannot, obviously, reverse time but we can think of our last movement with the right foot. The right foot will thus start the reversed motion to sit. It has not taken you long to become aware that the pelvis is moved first to lift the right foot off the floor. Now move the pelvis first to detach the right foot from the floor, taking the leg with its knee bent down to the floor to the spot where you sat to begin with. Review the entire procedure in your mind and, when this is more or less clear, sit on the floor. Tilt your knees to the left and visualize swinging them to get up moving to the right in the same way as you did so many times getting up to the left. If you cannot become aware of the pelvic spiral upward motion to the right rear of yourself, stop, rest, and tilt your knees to the right to rehearse the former side. Tilt them to swing left and this time get up again in that one gliding movement you know. Lift and move your right foot again, directing the pelvis back to the floor, tilt your knees to swing to the right. *Stand on your right knee* swinging your left arm forward and up to the right and see your pelvis moving in a spiral upward to the right to carry your left leg and foot to bear your full weight. As your pelvis carries both legs, your right leg also will straighten to share in bearing your weight.

Now lift your left leg by moving the pelvis and sit on the floor, swing your knees to the left and stand up without becoming fully erect. Move the pelvis to carry the right foot back to sitting, swinging your knees to the right, get up in one continuous spiral movement of the pelvis first downward and then upward to the right. You thus stand, sit, and stand again in one wink and in one motion. The pelvis never stops moving, as before sitting it already turns to swing the knees on its upward spiral on the other side.

You may now examine the illustrations. Think of your reading as being similar to learning the standard copybook-writing. Once you are familiar with the complex changes of movement, pressure, form, and directions you start forming your personal handwriting. It will never be like anyone else's handwriting. It need only be legible; that is, sufficiently well formed to make your intentions clear and unmistakable. You can now go back to the movement and make it catlike, smooth, and fascinating in your own way. Learn to be aware of the pelvis moving smoothly without breaking the continuous accelerating and decelerating parts, from standing through sitting to the next standing in the other direction. You can now become aware that the limbs arrange themselves ideally to follow the intended pelvic motion. The awareness you have gained in this learning will be cardinal and will stand for a wealth of other movements, even those you have learned before by trial and error and maybe have never followed up to the exhilarating speed and fluency you have obtained now. If you do not hurry but attend to the elimination of hindrances to motion, your speed will increase to beyond that of your weight freely falling. One can, in effect, project the pelvis downward and gather a momentum greater than the result of free falling. There is practically no limit to the quality of performance that Awareness through Movement will not transcend. The process of

You will find it more and more comfortable to lift the pelvis.

Continue the pelvic movement in its spiral ascent until it raises the right hip joint sufficiently to straighten the right knee.

Tilt your knees to swing to the right.

. . .Tilt your knees to the right.

 →  →

with your knees spread a little
rt until there is room.

Find out which hand on the floor
becomes useless when you tilt your
knees ... and can be lifted without
making anything more dfficult.

 ←  ←

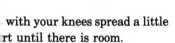

r pelvis moving in a spiral up-
d ... carry your left leg ... to
your full weight.

Stand on your right knee swinging
your left arm forward and up.

both knees to your right using
feet as hinges.

Tilt your knees to the left and back
to the right.

up without becoming fully

Your right leg also will straighten
to share in bearing your weight.

Your right foot will stand on the floor.

It will complete its rotation until you are facing what was your rear standing on your feet.

... on the floor

... to sit on the floor

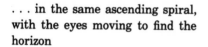

. . . in the same ascending spiral, with the eyes moving to find the horizon

. . . the ascent is completed.

Take the leg with its knee bent down to the floor to the spot where you sat.

Start the reversed motion . . . move the pelvis first to detach the right foot from the floor.

Put your hands behind you . . .
Bend your knees . . . Put the soles
of your feet flat on the floor.

Tilt
your

Sit, and stand again.

St
er

self-direction is being improved, and not any particular movement. The particular achievement is incidental and is a prize gained for better learning.

We may now have the patience to satisfy our curiosity. Sit on the floor with your right foot behind you on the right, knees spread apart to allow your left leg to lie between them, just as we did in the previous start. Lean on your left hand placed on the floor to the left of your pelvis on the spot where you find it will support your body most comfortably. Lift your right arm with elbow slightly bent to raise your forearm. The hand hanging downward is lifted to eye level at a comfortable distance in front of you. Freeze your trunk, your head, and your right arm with your eyes fixed on your hand, and turn the whole to your left to the angle that feels as if no effort is involved to do so, and stay thus, slightly twisted to your left. Breathe quietly with little externally visible movement. After a minute or so turn your eyes to the right; move the eyes only, keeping all the rest motionless. Move your eyes to focus on the hand, and then again to your extreme right, but without forcing yourself above the simple movement of the eyes. Repeat this shifting of the eyes to the hand and to your extreme right a dozen times. Stop. Close your eyes, resolve to stop moving immediately you become aware that you are increasing your exertion, and lift your arm with the hand in front of your closed eyes. Move, turning to the left without any restriction besides the one made. Turn only once to whatever angle you will, stop, open your eyes and you will realize that you have turned several or many degrees more to the left than at the beginning. Stay there.

Keep your eyes on your hand and move only your head to the left as easily as you can. Repeat a dozen times, moving the head only. Do this by first turning your head and eyes to the left, and then moving only your eyes back to focus on the hand. Again, cease and close your eyes and sit in the first position. Resolve to stop moving as soon as you become aware that you need a greater effort and, lifting your hand in front of your eyes, twist yourself to the left to open your eyes, and find that you have effortlessly twisted yourself through a bigger angle than before. Stop to think how different this is from usual experience. The "exercising" was in direct opposition to where the improvement was wanted, yet it did, in fact, improve. After a rest on your back, during which you become aware that your two sides do not lie the same way, you will realize that one of them has changed through what you have just done.

Sit again as before. Twist yourself comfortably to your left, lean on your left hand, and put your right hand on top of your head. Move the head assisted by your hand as if to touch your right ear on your right shoulder. Reverse the movement to touch your left ear on your left shoulder. The movement becomes easier and more extensive if you become aware that, while your right ear moves toward your right shoulder, the pelvis is rocking so that your right side becomes shorter while the ribs on the other fan out. The hand moves the head the other way round, and the pelvis and side move the other way round. After a dozen bendings right and left close your eyes. Sit in the original position and with your right hand in front of your eyes, and with your resolve to stop immediately you feel you are straining, turn, stop, and you will realize that you have twisted even more. How come? It is again an improvement, with unorthodox training.

Sit in the original position, twist to the left, but this time place both your hands on the floor to the left. Organize yourself to lean on both hands equally; they should be shoulder-width apart on the floor. Twist your shoulder girdle to the left, while turning your face, i.e. head and eyes, to the right. Become aware of the movement of the right hip joint and buttock to start the shoulder girdle motion. Watch the sensation in the spine. Undo the twists and rehearse a dozen times. As you sit, lift your right hand in front of your eyes and turn left at your discretion. You are very likely twisting yourself to look straight behind you. Compare this with your initial twist and you will realize that Awareness through Movement is a more efficient way to learn than just striving and willpower.

Short of writing another book, suffice to say that you have been differentiating eye movement and head movement, which means you have learned to move them in opposite directions. Most people stop their neuromuscular-spatial apprenticeship after moving both in the same direction. The same differentiation occurred between your pelvis and your head and eyes.

Sit. Tilt your knees to the right, leaning on your hands behind you. Swing your knees to the left to get up swiftly, moving your pelvis in the familiar spiral upward movement to the left to stand up, reverse, and stand up again to your right. Continue the complete cycle of standing-sitting-standing and you will soon become aware that the movement to one side is smoother and faster than to the other. Is there any relation to the direction of movement in the last lessons?

Now, sit with your legs to the left and rehearse all the steps of twisting trunk, head, eyes, and pelvis as before, but with one important restriction: make no movement at all at each step except adopting the new position. Sit still, imagining that you are actually moving but without doing so. You will become aware of the muscles being organized in the necessary patterns for performing the movement. If you go through all the steps in this way you will be surprised to find that your twisting to the right has improved and is even better than before. Moreover, it will have been achieved in about one-fifth of the time.

Now that you know what Awareness through Movement means you will appreciate the way it is presented, which provides a good chance for learning to occur. I asked Will Schutz of *Encounter* fame, who first brought me to the United States, to come with me to an interview at *New Dimensions.* Here are a few pertinent extracts.

WILL SCHUTZ: I find that your method is what I would call a self-oriented method, as opposed to a guru-oriented method. When I was doing some of your lessons, one particular example stood out. The problem was how to put my feet apart so that they were most comfortable. You told me to put them very close together and feel what that felt like and put them very far apart and see what that felt like, and keep moving them back and forth until it felt right. Whatever felt right, was right, was correct. I also have a thorough Arica training, which I consider a guru-oriented approach. Oscar Ichazo is the guru and you do what he says. I was doing the same thing there, except the rule was that you put your feet one elbow-length apart. If you did not do that, then the instructor would come along and say, "That's not right. You did not get it correct." What was right there was to remember what I was told to do and do it properly.

MOSHE FELDENKRAIS: I never force anyone to accept my view. I would never say "this is correct" or "this is incorrect." To me there is nothing correct. However, if you do something and do not know what you are doing, then it is incorrect for you. If you do know what you are doing, then whatever you do is correct for you. As human beings, we have the peculiar ability which other animals do not, and that is to know what we are doing. That is how we have freedom of choice. Suppose I see you placing your feet apart at a distance which I consider incorrect. Now, why do I consider it incorrect? Not because I think it should be a certain length, but because I feel that you are really uncomfortable, and are standing that way only because you have never actually visualized what distance is necessary in order to feel comfortable. You are not really concerned with comfort. If you were very shy or if you were a virginal girl you would hold your feet together because it is prescribed as being "decent." If you are a show-off extrovert wanting to show how important and free you are you will open your legs much too wide. Much too wide for whom? Not for me. I do not say "this is right" and "this is wrong." I say that if you know that you are holding your feet close because you are shy, and you feel awkward spreading them more, then there is no harm. From my point of view, it is correct that you should do what you like. I am not here to tell you what to do; I am here only to show you that you should know what you are doing. However, if you do not really know that you hold your feet like that, and you believe that all human beings should hold their feet together, and you are virtually unable to open them, not because your physiology or your anatomy does not permit it, but because you are so unaware that you do not know that they can be opened, then it is incorrect.

WILL SCHUTZ: I remember an example in one of the lessons I took with you where that was illustrated. We were following some instructions, and one person in the class would not do it the way you said. Rather than bawl him out, you asked the rest of the class to do it the way he did it, then do it the way you said, and judge for ourselves which was more comfortable. The process helped us to increase our awareness of what actually felt better.

MOSHE FELDENKRAIS: There is more to it than that. My point was this. I said something, and the great majority of people did it in one way. There was one who somehow interpreted the same words quite differently. Now, it is possible that he was an idiot, that he could not understand what I was talking about. That is alright. However, I believed that he was not an idiot, that instead he was so far away from being able to function as I asked that he could not conceive that I meant what I said. Now, all the other people did it as I asked, and I told all of them, "Look, look how this person does it. Maybe he is right; perhaps it should be done like that. Can you imitate him?" Yes, everbody could. "Can you do it the way you did it before?" Yes, they all could, but he could only do it his way, and not like all the others. Hence, they had the freedom of choice between two acts, but he was compulsive, unable to change. He did not know what he was doing and he could not do what he wanted. That technique, making you to look at him made it easy for him to look at himself. I could say to him, "Look you have done it as you have. Maybe you are right. These people can do like you, or can do something else, but you have no choice. You are a computer; they are human beings. They have free will; they have choice. You have not. Now, sit and look. Can you see?" By seeing the others imitating him, he suddenly realized that he did not know what he was doing. As soon as he realized that, he did it exactly like all the others. His learning took ten seconds. He recaptured his freedom of choice and regained human dignity.

Understand that there are two sorts of learning. There is the kind of learning which is committing things to memory; for instance, taking a telephone book and learning it by heart, or taking an anatomy book and learning the attachments and origins of each muscle. That learning is independent of time and experience. You can decide to do it at any time. But suppose you want to play the piano. Every time you begin to learn, you say, "Look, all right, I did not play the piano as a child. Now it is so difficult to start it and what's the point of playing the piano. I am a scientist: I am a radio interviewer. What do I have to play the piano for? If I need piano playing, I listen to somebody playing the piano on records." But for some people, like Yehudi Menuhin or Vladimir Horowitz, the making of music is more important than your radio or your science. They learn by a type of learning which is almost beyond personal choice. You can learn the phone book if you want to, or not learn if you do not want to, and you can change your mind.

But there is learning in which you have no say whatsoever and that learning is latent in the natural laws which have produced our brain and our nervous system and our body and our muscles. These laws are included in the cosmic laws of the universe. They are so precise and so sequential that you have no say about the order you will learn them in. They must be learned in that order; if not, you will not develop as a normal human being. You will be a cripple or an autistic child, something not normal. Why can you not teach a baby even a year old to hold a pencil and write? The baby cannot write until the capacity develops.

You see, there is a kind of learning that goes with growth. You cannot skate before you can walk, no matter how clever you are, even if you are a genius. You must first learn to walk. You cannot walk before you crawl. If you learn to walk before you crawl you will be a cripple. You cannot learn to speak before you are vertical. You know why you cannot? In the human system each part comes into function in sequence one after another. The functioning helps the growth at each stage as a new part of the brain comes into dominance, and changes the entire way of action. This type of learning must proceed at its own pace. We have no say in it. However, because this learning is done under human direction, it may be done in a different way than was intended by nature.

My way of learning, my way of dealing with people, is to find out for that person who wants it what sort of accomplishment is possible for that person. People can learn to move and walk and stand differently, but they have given up because they think it is too late now, that the growth process has been completed, that they cannot learn something new, that they do not have the time or ability. You do not have to go back to being a baby in order to function properly. You can, at any time of your life, rewire yourself, provided I can convince you that there is nothing permanent or compulsive in your system except what you believe to be so.

I do not treat patients. I give lessons to help a person learn about himself or herself. Learning comes by the experience

of the manipulation. I do not treat people, I do not cure
people, and I do not teach people. I tell them stories because
I believe that learning is the most important thing for a
human being. Learning should be a pleasant, marvelous
experience. Very often in the lesson, I say, "Look, would you
stop? So many of you look so stern, as if you were trying to
do something terribly difficult and unpleasant for you. That
means you are tired, you will not understand any more.
Break it, and have a coffee. Or let me tell you a story so that
I can see the brightness in your eyes and a smile on your
face, and so that you will listen and find that what I say is
important to you."

WILL SCHUTZ: To me, that is not the main thing you do.
You do talk, and you do make these points, but the big thing
is what goes on with the hands. And to watch a Feldenkrais
lesson for me is almost a meditation. It is very quiet and
sensitive and it is in the hands where the things happen.
There is a communication from the body to the brain that
is going on without words, through the hands. The talk
usually comes later.

Summary

   All mammals, men included, have skeletal muscles which
are of no use at all without senses, especially without the most
important, the kinesthetic sense. All of this complexity is ut-
terly useless without the autonomic nervous system and the
central nervous system. To act, to move, to feel, to think, to do
anything (even speak), all of these structures must function.
Each of the items mentioned needs learning to acquire the
ability to have many modes of functioning for each sense—
feeling, thinking, moving, acting, reacting—if we are to live,
flower, and become happier as we grow wiser.
   We need habits if we are to act appropriately and quickly.

But habits used blindly or as if they are laws of nature, i.e. cannot be changed, are just perpetuated, agreed ignorance. The possible alternatives in our array of means, functions, and structures are staggering. Yet all unhappy sufferers "are made like that," i.e. like their habits. These make them blind to the enormous choice of alternatives available to them. Because habits are so useful and economic to use, we prefer not to change them.

A great variety of "habits" is available to every one of us. We could use some of them on Sundays and some on other days of the week, some of them when on your feet and some of them when in bed, and choose one for each affair. It is not so easy to help oneself as it may appear, but not as difficult as one may feel. If necessary, turn to people who make it their occupation to assist others with difficulties which they cannot see through by themselves.

FUNCTIONAL
INTEGRATION

Functional integration turns to the oldest elements of our sensory system—touch, the feelings of pull and pressure; the warmth of the hand, its caressing stroke. The person becomes absorbed in sensing the diminishing muscular tonus, the deepening and the regularity of breathing, abdominal ease, and improved circulation in the expanding skin. The person senses his most primitive, consciously forgotten patterns and recalls the well-being of a growing young child.

You may remember the stories that I have left unfinished: the boy who came into the world right hand first, the woman who had seen five or six specialists and continued to be in pain, and so on. Describing cases is somewhat like making an inventory, but what use is an inventory in the case of human beings? If I made my own, without writing my autobiography, just listing my present complaints, it would give you little clue as to how you could be instrumental in bettering my life. Could you improve my injured knees? Could you help me to recover my bygone superb eyesight? And suppose even that you could, what good would it do to me now? I would probably be more alert and feel more myself, but how could you do what I cannot achieve in spite of having seen many first-rate specialists almost everywhere in the world.

Let us examine a concrete case. A violinist of repute was shot by somebody who did the shooting in order that you and

I should not forget that the owner of the gun feels frustrated. An orthopedic surgeon with the cooperation of a neurosurgeon somehow patched up the violinist's shattered arm, the wounds healed, and it was time to take inventory of the damage. The verdict was that physiotherapy might help to bend the elbow and straighten the arm, but playing the violin was out of the question and, therefore, the sooner he sought and found another profession the better. It is possible, of course, that the injury severed the median nerve of the arm completely, and the missing tissues produced scars making stretching of the arm, let alone movement of the wrist and fingers, quite unthinkable, short of a miracle.

What I intend here is not to extol the merits of Functional Integration as compared with most, if not all, of the therapeutic means used in the world. I wish, however, to show that there is a different method of using ourselves which is incomparably above and beyond that which results from retaining our habitual cause and effect pattern of viewing the world. The alternative is quite expedient and often an easier way of coping with our problems or tasks. My contention is that very often there are better ways of thinking which open up new vistas and make the unthinkable real and put the impossible within our grasp.

Let us examine more closely how a child becomes a violinist of repute. At birth nobody can vouch for the future of the newborn. We know from recurrent observation that the baby usually grows and in the first years does all manner of things that adults do not do, and we see in this activity preparation for adulthood. The funny thing is that this kind of activity will, in fact, result in an adult of some kind. In the first two years, the preparation for adulthood seems very similar for most futures. The child's bones grow, the muscles keep pace with this skeletal growth, and the growing is influenced markedly by a multitude of factors of environment; crawling is taking place in space and the timing of the movements is quite stringent. You cannot crawl by lifting and moving the members by pure chance. Now the timing and the spatial configurations of the small body are dictated by the gravitational field that acts on this body as it does on any other solid body. In other words, the growth of the muscles and the skeleton is not just any growth, but a very specific one. It conforms to the continuous movement of the little body through familiarity, the influence of gravitation can be almost ignored. All we see are configurations that are familiar to us, being identical to the necessities of equilibrium, stability, and mobility which we have all learned before in the same way never thinking of gravitation.

Many other things happen which, because of familiarity, we fail to see. The child also eats quite differently from sucking, he pronounces syllables and words, handles all kinds of objects, sometimes quite adroitly and sometimes less so. Clearly the bones do not do these things alone; they are moved by the muscles and the muscles need bones to move. It is also obvious that the nervous system makes the bridge between the skeleton and muscles and the outside of the body: the gravitational field, space, time and the social environment, without which there would be no objects to handle, or words to say or hear. In short, the environment consists of you and I—sex is obviously in already—objects, space, time, gravitation, society, and culture.

We have almost forgotten our violinist. He also was a baby and a child. His bones and muscles would have grown quite differently if he had had no nervous system to mediate between him and the surrounding environment. The environment made of the many bits and pieces detailed above is perceived by the nervous system through the senses. This system will direct, organize, adjust, and adapt the rest of the body to react to the objects that are in the environment. The hands, the feet, the whole body will conform to the environment through the nervous system which, in turn, will know whether the action produced the change haphazardly or, as expected, both in the body itself and outside it.

In this laborious way the fingers have learned through contact with fiddles and strings to produce sounds which the system found agreeable, pleasant, or unbearable. The never-ending activity of our nervous system directs itself through our muscles and skeleton to move and act in an environment which therefore becomes part of ourselves. This environment will appear to us as we perceive it through our activity and will therefore be a reflection of what our nervous system needs to continue to move itself, to act and react to the changes that occur in a mobile changing environment.

One of the first things we learn and do is direct our eyes and our hands to that which is around us. What else could we do? And therefore direction is probably the most basic thought or movement. Where are you going? When are you going? If there is no "where" the "when" is meaningless. Our basic orientation is right and left, in short, turning around ourselves. Directing, pointing in a direction, persists even in demented people, without that they could not move at all and without movement animal life is, what?

Something that eluded us now becomes quite obvious. Our violinist has acquired a skill to move his fingers on an external object with a dexterity that enables him to hear and judge continuously while his hands and fingers are directed in patterns that the nervous system has formed by actually using an environmental object, his violin in the first place. The environment is as necessary to becoming a violinist (it cannot be done without one) as is the nervous system (no movement, no hearing, and no realization of one's body without it) and as is the body (no playing violin without fingers, hands, and sitting or standing). And if we add the place where he is playing, the direction he faces, for whom he plays, and who needs that playing, we can begin to understand what Functional Integration is about.

Luckily we have neurologists and surgeons who repaired some of the damage suffered by the arm. The same goes for psychiatrists and psychologists who could help if a change of profession for a violinist of repute is unavoidable. There is, however, only Functional Integration which has any chance (and I, my assistants, and students have helped many) to make the violinist play anew. And believe it or not, if I succeed, he will be a better violinist than he was before the damage. He will also perceive more clearly what he is doing with his good hand and therefore he will be more able to do what he wants. He can now reach a higher level of performance.

Any complexity can be comprehended provided we look at it bit by bit. Let us first examine in detail how we act and move, how we direct ourselves in general. This will enable you to follow me in Functional Integration and understand why I allow myself to speak so authoritatively about matters that are not at all simple or intuitive, or known *a priori.*

Animal life consists of organisms that are structured in such a way that the functions of self-reproduction, self-maintenance, self-preservation, and self-direction exist. To us this means animal life. The first three structure-functions existed, very likely, long before the appearance of animal life in any proper sense. Similar functions can be distinguished in very large and heavy organic molecules. But self-direction is a notion which is meaningful only when attributed to an individuum, i.e. to a being that has a membrane, a skin, a boundary separating it from the rest of the world. Once such a separation is formed we have the individualization of a being. It may be a very primitive one, or a very complex one. Such a separation means, at once, that some sort of commerce, some kind of exchange, must operate or be made by the individual being between that being and the outside world.

The boundary will allow some of the external stuff to enter into the individuum and some of the internal matter to be rejected to the outside. This exchange is biased to increase the viability of the being for a certain period until it ceases to live, when it is reabsorbed into the surroundings, whereby the boundary, the membrane, the individualization are resolved. Self-direction loses its meaning when there is no self or individuum to whom self-direction is of some sort of interest.

To humans, self-direction appears to be connected with our representation of ourselves being upright. The most elementary self-direction to an adult human being is to the right or to the left, i.e. turning around the spine as a vertical axis. The first movement that we observe in a baby still lying, is its turning toward us to see or return our smile. In other words, he learns to turn right and left as he needs or wants to. What happens is certainly not what we ascribe to it. The terms of reference are borrowed from ourselves and change what is occurring to our point of view. We all agree, however, that there is a vital connection between the baby's activity and what he will be doing with himself as an adult. The continuity between the two situations involves the nervous system, the body containing it, and the environment in which it will be moving.

Obviously there is something evolving, growing in the matter of the being, as well as in its functioning. The right and left turning of the adult—and at each period we look at him while he is becoming one—is much more complex than we care to think. The eyes, the head, the ears, the right and left legs, the muscles, the joints, and the soles in contact with the supporting ground are all informing the nervous system of the environmental situation. All this combined with the configuration of the self act so that the turning will be performed in a fashion that will not compromise upright standing in the gravitational field, and cause a break in the continuity of self-direction. I have described this as simply as I can put it in words. I can do all that adults do as well as you, who might not know what I have said or on the other hand may know much more about it than I do.

From the point of view of Functional Integration, it is important to understand that turning around the vertical axis is an act or a function that implies self-direction which has meaning only to a living animal in its environment. And that this turning enables the animal to accomplish all the four self activities as necessities or as exploratory movements or even as an apprenticeship or just for their own sake. If you need convincing that this is so, think of the coincidence, fact or design, that all the instruments serving, connecting our senses to the outside distant world are located in the head. Sight, hearing, smell are directional. To fix a direction and a distance we need two identical instruments separated by a distance between them. Our teleceptors are the sensors and the movers of self, orienting the head to a direction. The direction is where the head stops turning at the moment when the right and left organs produce equal signals on receiving equal stimulations. At such moments we look at the source of the change we saw, listen to the source of the noise that moved us, or the smell that intrigued us. Our head turns just so and just that much. How does the head, or we, know how to be so precise? Moreover, when we do turn our head to any such provocation from the environment we find that the skeleton, muscles, and our entire being have one side, the one to which we turned our head, toneful and strong, while the other is folding in its articulations. Our weight is shifted to the strong tonified side and we turn until our head is again in the middle and the asymmetrical muscular activity of the muscles turning the head is no more. Our self-direction is now free to start moving in any direction we may choose or be called upon to act again. Just think that our mouth also connects us to the environment beyond what we can touch. The mouth is also directional, though not so clearly as the teleceptors. It is difficult to think that such a major involvement of the entire organism including everything contained in the skull, all the muscles, and the skeleton could be achieved without apprenticeship. The turning of the head of the lying baby in response to the mother's efforts to evoke a response that will assure her that the baby knows who its mother is, is the beginning of the very long learning-growing process that will produce the marvelous results I have described. All that is perhaps more personally important to me than to you. I have already mentioned my wonder and admiration of people who worked, discovered, wrote, and told us about it. I also told you that my own contribution to these teachers of mine is that I have added to their teaching something that enables us to use their achievements here and now to make our life easier and better.

Magnus of Utrecht University in Holland has familiarized us with the tonic and righting reflex of ourselves. Functional Integration uses his genius in a way that would fill his heart with joy. Here it is. In the apprenticeship of right and left rotation around the vertical in upright standing, the crucial point of the learning is the arrival of the impulses sent by the nervous system in patterns such that all the intricate movements can be performed. Now, suppose something has gone wrong, say like in cerebral palsy, where practice and growth do not result in the usual simple intentional acts, or that injury has produced a similar difficulty. We have already seen that the violinist's injured arm was attended to and helped by qualified medical specialists. But the real problem was, how could he play the violin, with the excellency wanted, over and above the basic healing of the arm and hand? The real question is, how can we make the impulses from the nervous system arrive at their muscular destination in the right manner and strength?

In short, in all the examples, the sensory response and intentional motor activity are linked in the nervous system by the environment on the one hand, and the muscles and skeleton on the other. Any breach of continuity in the loop will interfere with or abolish functioning. In early babyhood, the continuity in the loop environment—sensation, nervous system, motor activity, environment and feedbacks from it—is intact in principle. Yet the baby cannot play the violin. One of the reasons is that the impulses are not differentiated sufficiently and the motor activity is not differentiated either. The responses and the intentional acts are global, not graded. All the members, hands and legs, move together and cannot form any finely directed act. Later, when the growth and the functioning gradually form a more specific passage for individual impulses in the synapses, more varieties of movement become possible. The fingers can be moved separately from one another. Different rates and intensities can be produced even in parts of the fingers. This discrimination between similar but slightly different movements is the differentiation we mentioned. Gradually, the synapses pass a greater number of impulses, each one to a different destination until the child can begin to practice writing and later practice playing the violin or whatever.

The important detail to understand is the multiple activity of the nervous system. It senses its own body and the objects of the environment and it has the curiosity to do these things. It repeats acts even if they are not successful and through the errors and slight adjustments slowly forms the paths through the synapses to write and play the violin. Learning occurs when the nervous system repeats its exploratory activity on an object of the environment until it is successful, i.e. satisfies the intention. There is thus a continuous interaction between the sensory and motor activities which are practically never independent. In hemiplegia through injury I can often pinpoint on the spine the precise location where the paralyzed person mistakes his right for left and vice versa. The inability to move the limbs is not only a motor failure, but is also a sensory trouble. Even if the muscles could function, the intention to use the right would feel like intending to move the left limb. Professor Bach-y-Rita of Stanford University witnessed such a finding when I taught in San Francisco. It is easy to follow the rationale of Functional Integration when treating cerebral palsy or in recreating a violinist who has lost his excellency through injury.

Let us return to the Parisian cerebral palsy girl you already know. Her hands are continuously active; her knees knock together, as her heels cannot touch the ground; and she walks on tiptoe with the feet turned exaggerately inward. The range of movement in the hip joints is restricted and the lumbar spine is stiff and unyielding. As you probably remember, she is a bright girl. Were she not, as is often unfortunately the case, it would be a much longer job. Sometimes it is a thankless enterprise and only an alleviation is obtained, which will gradually vanish if the child is left untreated for any prolonged period of time. Surgeons will often try to help by lengthening the Achilles tendons—heel cords—so that the feet can bend at the ankles a little more easily and thus enable the heels to reach the floor. I have seen two children who have each had this operation performed three times, first at the age of four, then at eight, and again at twelve. Needless to say, the surgeon himself did not think the first and second operations did much good. Then, sometimes the lengthening of adductors —the muscles that enable us to squeeze our knees together— is performed. This operation with braces on the legs will, of course, help the child to stand somehow in an improved manner. My criticism of the decision to operate is often answered by, "What else can one do? At least something is being done to make the child stand better and waddle about more easily." This is a valid argument but it shows that no alternative ever crosses the mind. The premise is that the brain was injured because of lack of oxygen (anoxia) during the delivery, and some believe that such things happen when a child is already weak before birth. And it seems reasonable to think that injury can be patched up by eliminating the most obvious misfunctions through as many operations as there are obvious defects.

Functional Integration approaches the problem from a new

direction entirely. An average baby cannot walk without moving while growing. At each period of this growth, quite different movements are performed by all babies. The movements result in the end in walking, standing, and so on. But none of the movements are "exercises" of the final movement. They are movements which are dictated by the state of the nervous apparatus, the muscles, the skeleton, and the "body" configuration which is feasible at that moment. Nervous systems would not exist in animals if these systems did not assist them to face up to the perpetually new necessities and new opportunities that the environment presents. I have already mentioned the order-seeking function of the nervous system. It is this order-seeking quality that enables a child to find a final mode of action through erratic activity of now one and then another constituent of standing or of any other function, just as in later learning, say to ride a bicycle, the learner, to begin with, does all the movements that interfere with riding. He will inhibit one by one the parasitic, useless, indiscriminate, and unintentional parts of his movements until he discovers the essential, orderly, intentional, differentiated, final version. Thus, the learning of skills (swimming, singing, juggling, or whatever) when young is a general, confused, ill-directed activity in which the nervous system discovers an orderly activity after having inhibited all the failure-producing, erratic, uncontrollable, jerky moves. I have persisted in this labored description so that you can follow and understand how a cerebral palsy, intelligent child or person can be helped to learn finally what other children learn in their childhood. Suppose that, after examining the cerebral palsy girl I mentioned before, I find that lying on her back is the easiest position for her. I will let her lie on the couch which has a felt-covered hard-soft surface, and put a roller or a sponge under her knees so that they are supported firmly and safely. She is then in the position in which the antigravity muscles—mostly extensors—do not have to lift any weight. Lift your own elbow and hold it in the air, and after a minute or two lower your elbow to rest on the table or any other firm support, and your shoulder muscles will decontract as their work is now done by the support. Nervous systems tend to efficient economic functioning.

Therefore, all parts of the girl's body, the lumbar regions, the nape, the ankles, all will be supported, asymetrically if necessary, until she is lying firmly supported all along her skeleton in a way she would lie if she had no muscles at all. The nervous system is not receiving any stimulation from the soles of the feet: there is no compression of the joints of the ankles, knees, hips, and so on. The tendons are not stretched, the head is not carried, and it does not look, listen, or speak and neither is it orientated by what occurs in the environment. In essence, the tendency of the nervous system to optimal functioning coincides with minimal stimulation. The nervous impulses to the musculature will quieten down. The intentional cortex will be freer to "new pattern-forming" than when everything in the system is engaged in some sort of activity, be it intentional or automatic habitual.

I now have a malleable entity before me with a large number of possibilities. I can alter the shape of the pressure pattern which the poor use of the system has called for. I say this, but it is in part nonsense, for I cannot achieve alterations so that different impulse patterns reach all the muscles. I can only touch, pull, push, press, palpate, and so forth and do all these things in a way that is more orderly, more like quieting the system as happens in young babies and children when lying at ease. I am able to make repeatable consistent stimulation and feel whether the nervous system I am handling can respond in a way that is different from the starting response. I can feel after twenty or fewer repetitions that the lying person recalls the pattern he or she is used to and can feel the forming of a new neural organization. This is real progress, for the nervous system is now responding normally to a neutral environment. Cerebral palsy functioning, excited, jerky, athetotic, erratic, does not respond to the stimulation of the environment in the orderly fashion as an intact system does, but here on the couch the cerebral palsy child responds for the first time as all normal children would.

Then there is the most important part of the body, the position of which causes the distribution of tonus to the entire musculature in standing and all other movements of a person. I am talking about the head. It is a heavy part of ourselves which, as I have said already, bears all the instruments we need to relate to space, sound, light, and smell. No movement is undertaken with the head lying still and all the teleceptors inactive. We turn our head right and left when there is the most insignificant change in the environment attracting our attention, and also for the intention of executing the minutest movement whatsoever, let alone rapid, powerful actions and reactions. The reader can refer to any modern book on physiology, or reread my book *Body and Mature Behavior* to learn how the rotation of the head affects the tonus of the entire musculature and how sudden loss of balance evokes the righting reflex of the eyes and the head itself. I can place my hand on the front of the head of the lying person and move it very gently to the right and to the left. In a body of a human who is both intellectually and emotionally a genius, and whose senses are as good as his feeling, the head will yield to the slight motion of my hand with the smoothness of movement found in the best handmade Swiss watch you can buy. The head of a person suffering from cerebral palsy can be moved in this fashion only a fraction of an inch to one side and another fraction of an inch to the other. The head is unable to deal with the environment uniformly well. It has only particular directions in which it moves so that the body follows it. In all the others, the head is rigidly held. No smooth movement can be performed, except strictly in the limited directions where the head is more or less fluent.

I have examined many thousands of heads of supposedly

normal healthy individuals. Only a few dozen of them, all extraordinary human beings and each a hallmark in his activity, yield to the motion of the hand to rotate the head right and left with remarkable smoothness and ease. I have already mentioned some of them. The great majority of people fall between the extraordinary and the sufferers from cerebral palsy. To be concise, people never reach their endowed potential excellence except in a few cases.

The person lying before us is handicapped because she has been unable to make head or tail of her erratical widely wandering movements. She has not succeeded in finding a repetitive similarity from which she could form a clear and better way of acting. I therefore substitute myself for her early environment, both gravitational and human, by making movements of her head which are similar to one another so that even the erratic functioning will, in the end, recognize an orderly possibility. To do that I have, probably, to continue the initiated, gentle, hardly recognized rotary movement of the head with one hand, while with the other reach lower parts of her body where the rigidity is even greater. This rigidity makes it impossible for the head to perform a large or smoother rotation. A Milwaukee brace, or a cast on a healthy thorax will cause the rotation of the head to be so restricted that it resembles a bad case of cerebral palsy. Even in a plain skeleton the seven cervical vertebrae cannot be made to twist much without dislocating them from one another! The twelve thoracic vertebrae also twist very little but the lumbar five can twist more than the others. Only the axis and the atlas— the two upper cervical vertebrae—twist significantly even in, say, Bechterev disease or deformant osteoarthritis. They are the last to go and practically never fuse to the end.

As I repeat slowly the gentle moving pressure on the forehead, and assist myself with my other hand to facilitate the rotation by moving the sternum, the ribs and, if necessary, also the pelvis, all to increase rotation of the head, one direction improves first, as the head moves with increasing ease and through a larger angle of rotation. The entire side becomes softer and moves more easily, the eyes open wider, and the breathing is easier, involving parts that were held rigidly before.

Once the lying person realizes the facilitated movement of the head and the parts below, there will often be a deep sigh of relief. The other side is now dealt with in the same manner. It takes me from ten to fifteen minutes to enlarge the angle of rotation from a barely perceptible movement to a range of twenty to thirty degrees both ways. The head is now held with both hands and is lifted from the couch; it is lifted and oriented until it sits on the lying body as it would sit on a healthy body standing with good posture. This usually allows the diaphragm to move and the lower abdominal wall begins to heave up and down. The breathing is obviously eased and more rhythmical. Next time it is much easier to achieve the better functioning, it will take only minutes to obtain evidence of further improvement. Repetition is not a very efficient way of essential learning, but it is useful as a means of familiarizing an already achieved learning. Learning is concerned with the unknown becoming known which is realized after its discovery. I may repeat for a couple of minutes the final achievement of the first session in the second or third meeting. The helped person should feel a friendly hand and attitude rather than any sensation of being pushed or manipulated. At each meeting something new, unforeseen, and unexpected will be used. The person's system will be alert, curious, and interested all the time, otherwise there will be stagnation and boredom, with no learning worth the trouble.

Many, if not most, cerebral palsy children and adults have spastic hands and fingers. The wrists are often rigid and cannot bend. Generally, it is the rotation of the ulna or the cubital bone of the forearm round the radius that is not possible. The ulnar bone is the one at the side of the small finger of the hand, the auricular finger. The radius is the larger bone at the thumb side of the forearm. This lack of rotation of the forearm means that the elbow is not moving well either. Obviously the shoulder blade and the clavicle of such a forearm are far from being ideal or even good. In short, a person with cerebral palsy has cerebral palsy all over, only some parts are a greater handicap than others. The shoulders and the arms being as they are, the learning of adequate intentional use of them is not possible. I have already given the reasons and even repeated them.

I will take, say, the right hand of the lying person and move it across his chest. Usually the arm will not yield to my gentle pull. I will cease my pulling, and repeat it even more slowly but this time I will use my right hand to support the elbow of the spastic arm. With both hands—pulling at the wrist and pushing at the elbow—I will move the right forearm across the chest in the direction of the left jaw or cheek, but only so much as can be done without having to increase my power. Then I will move it back to its normal position without releasing my holds. I will wait for the next breath. If, after several minute movements, I do not then feel the pulled (and elbow-assisted) arm following my action more readily and more extensively while I keep reducing my intensity with each repetition, I will slide my right hand under the shoulder blade, letting go of the elbow. Assisting the shoulder blade in the direction that eases the pull on the wrist, I will again help the wrist in the direction of the left cheek. Normally, the wrist will follow after about twenty or so more and more delicate attempts to reach almost the chin. At this moment I will let go of the shoulder blade and take the elbow for another movement or two, and then letting go of the elbow I will turn the head as much as it will go easily to meet the mounting wrist. At the finish, the palm will end up lying on the left cheek. At this point I will again hold the elbow and shift my left hand from the wrist to apply slight pressure at the back of it so that the palm lies on the cheek clearly and squarely. If I cannot help the person to achieve this I will give it up for the moment. Next time I will proceed differently altogether. In a more or less usual case of cerebral palsy it is possible for the palm to touch the mouth, the cheek, and stay there, with my right hand assisting the elbow and my other hand pressing the back of the hand to the cheek.

Having reached this far, the cerebral palsy person himself can learn to do the movement and can achieve it quite readily. The idea behind the whole action is that all babies at the start do not intentionally move their members and their muscles in a differentiated way. I mean, a baby will move both his fists to his mouth. He cannot, at the start, move one hand to his mouth and scratch his head with the other. It is a long gradual process of functioning while growing before the nervous system is capable of directing impulses through synapses, through a particular dendrite. To perform a simple movement like rubbing the end of the thumb against the end of the index finger intentionally, the inhibiting of the neighboring fingers to immobility so that a clear wanted delicate movement can be formed, the baby will for a considerable time, move many things together. Thus before a baby will put his right palm on his left cheek of his own initiative, for whatever reason or intention, many months of growth and learning without a formal teacher will go by. First, he will bring both fisted hands to his mouth. Then, in the course of time, bring them to his cheeks, and later use only one hand without the other. The child will learn bits of things from one teacher of his choice, somebody he likes, and the next bit from somebody else, and other bits will just dawn on him. He is so involved or interested that he feels the action he is performing, and keenly senses what is being wrought by him outside himself. Thus, a gradual differentiation takes place where there was once only a global, coarse, ill-directed motion.

You may now realize that while I am pressing the cerebral

palsy person's right palm to his left cheek with my left hand, assisting his elbow, and then his shoulder blade with my right hand, his head will rotate while the shoulder muscles and everything between the shoulder and the head plus the right corner of his chest will move together globally as one entity. This is reminiscent of the state of babyhood where the muscles joining the arm to the head have nothing to do, for in touching fists to mouth, the baby moves his head and shoulders by twisting his thorax. Similarly, the head-shoulder muscles are not involved in any activity when I am handling the cerebral palsy person as I have described. The nervous system as we have seen, will take a few minutes or ten to twenty rehearsals to recognize it has the ability to leave all these muscles quiescent. This is, maybe, the first occasion in a lifetime that the cerebral palsy person feels no movement occurring in a region that had never stopped contracting, with or without the slightest intention to do anything.

I use primitive nondifferentiated movements and reactions. Many of them are stored as a sort of engram in our system, and are not used by the average healthy person. The sucking reflex is a good example: a baby pokes his lips while reaching for the nipple. The adult will organize his lips in much the same way while uttering a long oo-oo sound, like in 'good' or 'hoo-hoo'. Some children may continue the sucking motion of their lips for an appreciable time after they have stopped feeding by sucking. However, most adults use sucking intentionally only. On the other hand, a traumatized adult, deeply disturbed emotionally, or actually suffering a nervous breakdown, will often poke his lips as in sucking and involuntarily repeat the sucking movement several times if his upper lip is stimulated by snapping it rapidly and suddenly. This dormant, now useless action was in its own time, the most vital and important movement.

I use many movements and reactions that were used in infancy and given up and stored in the normal way in the memory bank. I may evoke the protective stretching out of the arms when falling face down in order to organize the intentional stretching of arms which have never straightened before. To do that I have to support and guide the elbow, wrist, and shoulder to respond to my stimulus of the hand in the normal way. The cerebral palsy person learns to recognize a repetitive pattern he is performing unintentionally until he can actually do it unaided himself. The nervous system normally learns in a similar way, but the cerebral palsy system is unable to achieve such learning alone by itself, because of the wild discrepancies between similarly intended movements. It is hard for the person, if not impossible, to see any clear pattern emerging from attempts which are only nearly similar in all his learning situations.

I have evolved a large number of such means, situations, and movements sufficient to meet any usual cerebral palsy inability. One such means or technique is an artificial ground or floor. This is an effective auxiliary for organizing standing and walking in a variety of cases. I will describe it in detail to make it easier for you to grasp the wider thinking behind the use of Functional Integration.

Muscles that have not been injured from the outside usually function well unless there is some sort of disturbance or illness in the nervous system. The arrival of impulses of the intended action through the nerves to the muscles in the normal way is the problem in most muscular dysfunction. Normally our intention is sufficient to provide the complex impulse patterns programming all our movements. Our intentions spring most of the time from the environment through our sensory apparatus, and much of our ability originates this way. It is not always at all easy to decide whether a particular movement has originated as an immediate response to a provocation from the environment, or if we ourselves have initiated the stream of motor activity. From the start there is a continuous commerce between the growing organism and its changing environment. Even if we feel certain that we wished and initiated the movement ourselves we may come to doubt it if we look at the process of our life before the moment in question.

Movement failures may be due to defects in the sensory or motor parts of our makeup or in both. In Functional Integration I attend primarily to the function that is sought, the sensory and motor details have value and importance only because they are needed for accomplishing the function. It sounds like splitting hairs, and when we have no trouble it is indeed splitting a hair. But when we have to recover lost functioning it becomes of paramount importance, for how are we going to make impulses started by our intention arrive at their destination when there is a gap, a break in the continuity of the channels or paths they normally travel? Here is how I use the artificial ground or floor. The person lies on his back supported safely, as already described. His feet protrude a few inches beyond the couch, just enough to be able to see his heels over the edge. I then take a board, a foot and a half long, a foot wide, and thick enough to feel rigid; in fact, like a cheese board. Holding this board with both hands and facing the soles of the feet, I move it toward the feet, concentrating on one of them. I hold the board vertical, close to the foot and move it further forward until it comes into contact with the small toe. I break the first contact and reestablish it as many times as necessary to obtain quivering of the second toe. I then incline the board to touch the small toe only, then to contact the two together, and so on until the third, fourth, and finally the big toe all touch the board. Once all the toes are touching, I move the board to contact the heel only, then back to the toes, continuing like this until I observe action in the ankle joint, or a smoother one if there was one, then I will incline the board to touch the outer part of the foot on the side of the small toe. I touch alternately the big toe side alone and then the small toe side alone, until I feel a turning of the foot and then a softening, and more or less normal movement in it. The foot moves to stand firmly on the sole as if standing on an inclined floor or one that is not flat and has tiles inclined at different angles.

A healthy, well-coordinated organism can negotiate sand, pebbles, and all forms of ground, undulating, mounting, or descending, and of course the legs, pelvis, and head align themselves correspondingly to restore safe standing all the time. The person lying on the couch has the antigravity muscles quiescent as there is no stimulation for standing except the one I am producing with my board. All the interoceptive nerve endings in the joints, muscles, and tendons throughout the body act only as much as my stimulations on the side of the foot simulate walking on uneven ground. When these stimulations extend to the entire sole and my changing of the inclination of the board is slow enough to allow the adjustments resulting from the would-be changes of the ground, I can feel the entire leg behaving as it would if the person was really standing. In about thirty minutes I can obtain tonus changes in the same side of the whole body as the leg I am dealing with. The change will spread to the neck muscles and to the eyes as the head becomes involved in keeping balance. I thus obtain the dispatch of the trains of impulses in the body for standing on one leg. If there is no normal through passage and arrival of impulses to the musculature of the leg and the sole, I initiate by the stimulation of the sole the sending of impulses which will travel to reach their destination, as they did earlier in the baby and the child. If there is any likelihood of recovery, it works much better than just passively or actively manipulating the parts of the body. Applied passive movements have little chance of forming new passages in the dendrites of the synapses. On the other hand, exercises in walking with active striving involve movements wildly different from the ones needed and in the best cases will produce only a badly distorted standing and walking. Sometimes the person may recover himself without my board. The board technique, however, is not only an enormous timesaver, but it also brings about the best functional recovery of the quality of movement. Attending to the function in its entirety will activate and simulate in a harmonious way everything necessary for normal learning of sensory motor excellence as it happened originally. The artificial ground technique may succeed when everything else fails. Moreover, it works wonders on the average person whom we tend to call normal instead of average.

Maybe, by personal experience, you would convince yourself better of the effectiveness of acting in the way I have described. Stand in your socks or bare feet near a wall. Turn to face the wall. Put your right hand on the wall, with the elbow slightly bent. Stand on your right foot and move the left foot back a little with the heel not touching the floor, just to keep the body in balance. You are then resting on the left foot as you would at the very moment you lean fully on the right foot during walking.

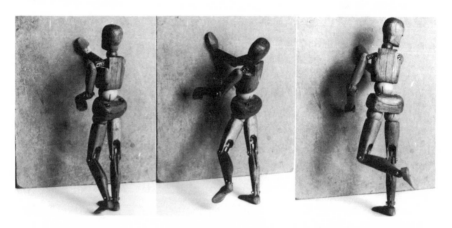

Stand as easily and as simply as you can. Now move your body so as to stand on the outer edge of your right foot: do not try too hard, just do it more or less. Next, proceed slowly and gently and turn your foot so as to stand preponderantly on its inner edge, and back onto the outer edge. Repeat the two movements a dozen times; each time you change the position of the right foot, reduce useless effort in the right arm and hand and breathe freely. Now lift your right heel off the floor then change a little and lift the forepart of the foot—with the toes—off the floor standing on the heel alone. Alternate these two movements five or six times. Breathe freely and do another five or six eversions and inversions of the foot, as at the beginning. I hope you remember to use your left foot only for keeping balance, with the heel not touching the floor. Now walk normally and note the difference between your right side and leg and the left side. You can begin to judge the effectiveness of what changing the pressure distribution on the sole of the foot would be if you were lying instead of standing. Even so, you can now sense a sufficient difference of tonus in the muscles of your entire right side.

Examine the pictures with easy attention. See how the head is turned, the pelvis, the lifted leg, the hand leaning against the wall.

Use your imagination to figure out all the other possible configurations. Proceed slowly when acting—making a small start of the movement and then increase the range. It will take you ten or eight attempts to reach the limit of your present possibility. By going through all the combinations the same way, you will find all ranges increasing and exceeding your expectations. A general improved posture and ease of action will result.

If my appreciation of your imagination is mistaken, you need this sort of thing more than you know.

Summary

Functional Integration is essentially nonverbal. It is effective because the injured person who may have had surgery, laminectomy, or an amputation of a leg, cerebral palsy, or any of an inexhaustible variety of injuries has lost the ability to help himself. People in similar situations lose their self-confidence. Their self-reliance is so compromised that most treatment produces only superficial improvement, if any at all.

The deepest kinesthetic sensations formed in early childhood are affected. The person withdraws from what happens in the outside world and is completely absorbed with attending to the internally occurring changes. The smoother eye movements, the rotation of the head, the change of pressure distribution on the soles of the feet, the reduction of intercostal tensions, the completion of the antigravitational muscular patterns for a clear feeling of vertical upright standing cannot occur without a complete change of neural functioning of the intentional or motor cortex and of the sensory one.

The muscular tonus becomes more uniform and is lowered. A feeling of well-being prevails. The breathing becomes regular; the cheeks more colored. The eyes are brighter, wider, and moister, and sparkle. At the end, one rubs one's eyes as if awakening from a restful dream. Normal people are too busy and miss something that is priceless. They should try Functional Integration.

THE OBVIOUS
IS ELUSIVE

Many things are not obvious. Most psychotherapies use speech to get to unconscious, forgotten, early experience. Yet feelings go on in ourselves long before speech is learned. Some pay attention not to what is said but to how it is said. Doing this enables one to find the intentions behind the structure of the phrasing, so that one can get to the feelings that dictated the particular way of phrasing. In short, how one says what one does is at least as important as what one says.

Familiarity makes things, actions, and notions obvious. We are so familiar with speaking that everything about it seems obvious. Familiarity with our bodies makes most of our overall notions about it obvious. The same can be said about learning, thinking, dreaming, and about almost all the things we are familiar with. My contention is that speaking is not thinking, although we "obviously" consider them as the same thing. Most people have difficulty in admitting this to be correct. I would rather say that the obvious to us contains all our scientific ignorance, and it needs more fundamental understanding and relearning than anything we think we know.

We know very little and often nothing about most obvious phenomena. How is it that a box of matches looks to us the same size and form at any distance or position where it is still recognizable? How do we swallow? Young children can think long before they can speak. Helen Keller could certainly think before she learned her own way of speaking. Animals often behave so that we believe they can think even though they cannot speak. Speech, and even more the written or printed word, has played a part of inestimable importance in our development as a species. Many believe that it is comparable to our genetic endowment. Speech provides us with the information and the ability to do what other animals do instinctively. Human instincts are as weak as our bodies when compared with strong animals or even weak animals. Even so, thanks to speech we have available to us the experience of thinking. Our inheritance is so great—artistic creations, knowledge of our predecessors, immense cultural treasures in book form on mathematics, music, poetry, literature, history, sciences, geometry, anatomy, and medical writings in general, physics and so many other disciplines, philosophy, linguistics, semantics—that we have difficulty in deciding whether homo sapiens is the product of his biological makeup alone or consists also of his intellectual endowment made available because of speech in its different forms.

Yet, I contend that in self-knowledge speech is a formidable obstacle. When it is used in all the various therapies available to analyze people's minds it takes years to disentangle what goes on in us to make us say what we say, which is being analyzed. In self-knowledge one cannot get at fundamentals without undoing the link between thought and speech. We were not born with thought and speech being indistinguishable. As we spend much time in learning to speak, unnoticed to ourselves, we have acquired the erroneous notion that speaking and thinking are synonymous. Words are symbols and not signs, as in mathematics. When I say "I want" I may mean I desire, I need, or I lack. What do I think when I say "I want"? I believe that I am selecting from my thinking only one of several shades of meaning and that is the one that I wish to communicate to another thinking human. I discover a new shade which is obvious to me but speech is a means of communicating only one aspect of my thinking to somebody else. Therefore, unless I am very careful I may communicate an aspect of my thinking which I never intended to communicate. Moreover, my interlocutor may understand another aspect of it which I never intended although he clearly heard it. You can see how treacherous this ground can be! I say I want to be a writer, but on examining myself I find out that when I say "I want" I am only describing what I lack. I am not a writer, it is only a wishful thought or a desire, so to myself, as to my interlocutor, my speech is really not thinking but a vague symbol indicating a large domain or an assembly of notions which may even contain their negations.

Suffice to think what God, truth, justice, honesty, communism, fascism, and so on mean in different human societies to see that much of our trouble lies in the fact that we confuse speaking with thinking. Thinking is a much wider function which contains many forms of possible expression. Speech is a serial event, as words come one after the other in time and by their nature cannot communicate the thought which may contain an immense number of aspects. There is always more than one way of expressing a thought. Most irate discussions and differences between humans are due to confusing speaking with thinking. Nearly every delegate to a disarmament conference thinks that disarmament is desirable, otherwise there would be no conference. The thoughts are dressed in the garments of expression and what is said is so varied that nobody can recognize the thoughts in the speeches, as these thoughts may be so multiple as to necessitate several decades of pronouncements, speech being a serial event in time. It has always struck me as particularly incongruous that all the functions of the so many different constituents of the brain (corpus striatum, globus pallidus, the pituitary, amygdala, hypothalamus, thalamus, hippocampus and the two different hemispheres) should not have more than one set of muscles to operate. Sure enough, muscles can do more than one kind of contraction; there are muscular tremors, clonic movement, spastic contractions, etc. But should there not be some kind of corresponding localization of functions in the body and in its muscles? The fact that only one set of muscles serves all the different parts of the brain gives me a clue to understanding the unity of the nervous system and the localization of the different functions. The movement of animals as well as man shows a parallel organization. In the body, fingers and toes serve differently from elbows and knees, shoulders and hip joints. For any use of fingers, be it playing the piano, counting banknotes, or writing, we must displace the entire skeleton with all its muscles to the piano, to the bank, or to the desk. Delicate movements need wrists, fingers, ankles, and toes but the entire musculature is involved in bringing the finer extremities to the place where they perform. The shoulders and the hips are necessary where more power is needed, and they are involved in transporting the body to the place where delicate fingers are necessary. Elbows and knees particularly are involved in all the skills of the human body. But again, the entire self must be transported to jump, and hands must hold the pole for the vault. Roughly speaking, there is a difference between holding the pole and the vault itself. Localization of movement now becomes a hazy, far-fetched division.

In the same way, counting money is not localized anywhere in the brain any more than the fingers themselves are money-counters. In every action the whole brain is active as surely as the whole body is involved. Obviously the brain, having transported the entire body to the piano, then has to use the auditory apparatus, the motor cortex for the fingers on the keys, the feet on the pedals, the extensors for sitting, and the head . . . and the 'body' is used similarly.

The scheme would be of little interest were it not for the idea that as the body, in between any two activities whatsoever, must go through the upright standing configuration, so the brain too has a passing neutral configuration. It is the passage from one activity to the other that needs a cleaning of the slate, so to speak. Just as standing can be considered dynamic at a particular point in the process of moving, so the quiescence of the brain is necessary in passing from one activity to the other. I believe that cleaning the slate takes probably a few milliseconds and is, therefore, unnoticeable except when the switching is defective. Thus, I believe that ankle sprains and biting one's tongue occur when two actions follow each other before the slate is completely clean. These failures occur when we start a new intent while the former is not yet completed. Therefore, the new intent starts before the slate is completely clean. We thus perform two incompatible actions simultaneously.

Think what can be said about a triangle, when the thinking contains all that I know about it and even what I may discover. My interest in this dilemma or problem is practical. I have to communicate something which may help a person who is in trouble, or wishes to change his aches and pains, or is born with a cerebral palsy organism, or has been injured, or has acquired body habits which are self-directed (feeling inadequate) and self-destructive (feeling unworthy). I wish to convey something which may help the person to reorganize the acting of his self through the body with self-direction to make life easier, simpler, or even more pleasant and aesthetically satisfying. It is useful at this juncture to make the point that free choice is closely related to thinking and is gone when spoken and communicated to somebody else or even said to oneself, thereby making the decision. Free choice means essentially choosing between alternatives. In thought, we choose one alternative and communicate it, although several other choices may have existed in our thinking before we decided to dress one of them in words.

In life, no alternative means anxiety and often compulsion. Walk along one board of the floor. You can probably do that and see little point in doing so again at my suggestion, as you are sure that your recovery from any slight errors of balance will be good enough. You have no doubt because you have the alternative to step sideways, correct your balance, and go back to walk on the board. Raise the board in your imagination to one foot and see yourself walking along it; raise it to some ten feet in your imagination; or better still, try a single board poised on two supports and you will see that the elimination of alternatives—in this case no side-stepping—increases anxiety sufficiently to paralyze thought, let alone performance. Your doubt regarding the possibility of recovering balance is well founded, because your ability to balance has never been learned to that degree of excellence. Nevertheless, it can be achieved and someone has walked on a cable from one roof of the World Trade Building to the roof of the next building.

I repeat again, the important issue is that no alternative means anxiety. Free choice means having at least another way. Free choice is meaningless when we are compelled to adopt the one and only way we know. Free choice means having an alternative mode of action available, so you can then choose the way you want most. To elect not to act is really no choice at all—it is not life.

An intentional voluntary movement, say with your hand along a trajectory, can be stopped, recontinued, reversed, or moved to do something else. A voluntary movement means free choice. A defensive, reflexive movement is of the all-or-nothing type; it is primitive and without intention. Such a movement is valid only in the face of danger and self-preservation, and when there is no time for choice. Then we either preserve ourselves or are maimed or perish altogether.

As I suggested above, the obvious is elusive. When we try to reach the main source of our thinking we come to depths where it is not easy to see if the elusive is more obvious than the obvious. Thus, it is possible to consider that free choice exists only in the process of thinking. As soon as the thought leads to an action, albeit only saying it, the die is cast, and the choice is gone forever. Obviously more inquiry and clearer thinking are essential to understand why nervous systems are needed in the world. What is consciousness needed for, and would not just being awake do the job? Regaining consciousness after having lost it usually starts with the question, "Where am I?" Is knowing where I am, and is general knowledge of self-direction the conscious function of the nervous system? Would we understand the problem more fully if we knew in which part of the brain it is located?

Here we touch upon a very thorny problem. Localization of functions, say of speech or writing, in the brain has had so many successes that it is almost a heresy to cast any serious doubts on the correctness of the idea. Only a few consider function in large groups such as the hindbrain, the limbic system, and the forebrain. Nobody would seriously maintain that speech is a purely neocortical function located in the Broca area exclusively. However, elementary primitive muscular intentional movements are so located on the cortex that Penfield's homunculus is pictured in most good books on neurophysiology in all languages. The idea is so successful that more and more precise localizations are discovered and confirmed by different laboratories.

Any act can be complexed almost at will. Think of driving a car while smoking, without neglecting your friend at your side, and at the same time listening and seeing all around the car. Caesar and Napoleon are said to have been able to read, listen, and write three letters simultaneously. Yet we cannot act and not act at the same time, which on the face of it is less complex than the complicated situation of driving the car. Is it that an act involves the whole brain as it involves the whole body? Negating an act is somehow similar to changing direction of a moving body. A break, a zero velocity, is necessary in between switching from one to the other.

It may be wiser to stop here before sinking into even deeper waters, and speculate on a quantum of thinking and other functions of the brain. After all, it is a useful way to understanding most phenomena of energy and its materialization.

Summary

The more one deals with the obvious, the more one sinks into deeper waters where the elusive is paramount. The study of speech is now a preoccupation of many investigators. More precise knowledge of the origin of speech is necessary before we can use the word "obvious," and mean it.

IN A NUTSHELL

I believe that at this very moment there are something like a hundred people who think and nourish ideas similar to the ones dealt with in this book. I know some of those people personally. And in all of the workshops which I have directed over the last thirty-five years in many countries and involving hundreds, sometimes thousands of people, I have always found at least one person who has discovered in his own way the equivalent of my system. These facts convince me that I am moving in the direction most needed at this time.

The vastness of the practical possibilities that can be derived from my work and which are available now makes any one book too small for an adequate presentation of the essentials. My assistants, pupils, and myself have reached many tens of thousands of people in eight different countries. In the last three months we have worked in the United States, Sweden, Canada, Holland, France, Germany, Switzerland, and Israel. I have taught statesmen, actors, musicians, orchestral conductors, and people in all walks of life. I have helped victims of poliomyelitis, wounded soldiers, people injured in car and industrial accidents, swimmers, divers, children, and many senior citizens. Those stricken with seemingly incurable diseases and chronic dysfunction such as cerebral palsy, postural defects, and breathing troubles have been helped beyond their expectations. I hope I have presented at least the fundamentals of a teaching which is applicable to all men no matter what activities they perform. What has been achieved so far is only a faint beginning of what can and needs to be done.

Learning to foster individuality will make for a society of better individuals. Our thinking ability will improve because our brains will be wired in by an environment that is richer than ever before. Today electronic valves are replaced by transistors, chips making possible computers beyond the dreams of geniuses only a few decades ago. Individual thinking has also improved through teamwork. The ten percent use of our brains is a limitation from the past. Most people build their lives around the peaks of their organic learning, and this is the source of their limitations and poor overall use of themselves.

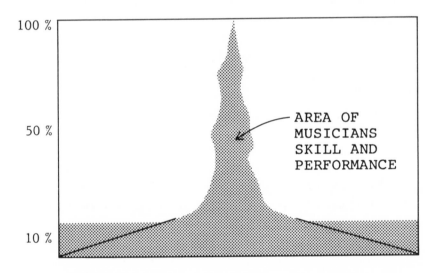

The diagram illustrates the development of an excellent musician, when the area of peak is still only ten percent of the area of his total ability. Each one of us has a peak or two and the rest is only potential.

Humanity passes through periods of crises: inflation, recessions, energy shortages, ecological troubles, so that what is ahead of us may be worse than we imagine. Increases in knowledge and ability have eliminated slavery and drudgery.

All the great civilizations of the past had the slaves essential for the growth of their culture. The Egyptians had slaves to build their pyramids, the Greeks had slaves to make Socrates and Plato possible, the Romans and Americans also had slaves for their drudgery. All this allowed the masters to learn, to build, to write, and to think.

It has taken almost until now before humanity can replace slavery in some form or other by automation, the most perfect slave one can imagine. But this unique opportunity will create more trouble than we can envisage. We shall have to relearn tasks we already know, and to pay for the necessities of life no more than we pay for the oxygen we breath. Automation and automatic factories will leave most workers without work. But to achieve such general automation you need a new caliber of brain which will take something like twenty-five years to form. Population growing as it does will cause the new twenty-five-year-olds to push over the fifty-fives and sixties into retirement no matter how clever they may be. In a slave-free society the middle aged will have to provide for the young until the age of twenty-five and for the old over fifty-five. We can now see that unless we learn to think about the things we know in alternative ways, unless we widen and deepen our freedom of choice and use it humanely, the real abolition of slavery will begin as a disaster.

The learning this book extols is a real necessity and must be popularized now. For this purpose the Feldenkrais Guild exists in San Francisco with over a hundred practitioners working in various states of the United States, in Canada, Europe, and Israel. In addition, the Feldenkrais Foundation in New York fosters the development of our work and produces films, videotapes, books, articles, and interviews for the media throughout the world. It is the avowed priority and aim of the Feldenkrais Foundation to publicize all available material in order that Awareness through Movement may be within the reach of everyone who wishes to better his and our lives.

BIBLIOGRAPHY

Bateson, Gregory. *Mind and Nature.* New York: E.P. Dutton, 1979.

Bernal, J. D. *The Physical Basis of Life.* London: Routledge and Kegan Paul, 1951.

Blechschmidt, Erich. *The Beginnings of Human Life.* New York: Springer-Verlag, 1977.

Clark, Le Gros. *The Antecedents of Man.* Edinburgh: Edinburgh University Press, 1959.

Darwin, Charles. *The Expression of Emotions in Animals and Man.* London: Murray, 1904.

Dunlop, Knight. *Habits: Their Making and Unmaking.* New York: Liveright, 1949.

Erickson, Milton. *Hypnotic Realities.* Irvington, N.Y., 1976.

Erickson, Milton. *Hypnotherapy.* Irvington, N.Y. 1979.

Fulton, John. *Functional Localization in the Frontal Lobes and Cerebellum.* London: Oxford University Press, 1949.

Hanna, Thomas. *The Body of Life.* New York: Alfred A. Knopf, 1980.

Huxley, Julian. *The Uniqueness of Man.* London: Scientific Book Club, 1942.

Keith, Arthur. *The Human Body.* London: Thornton Butterworth, 1912.

Monod, Jacques. *Chance and Necessity.* New York: Random House, 1977.

Ornstein, Robert. *On the Experience of Time.* London: Penguin Books, 1969.

Poincaré, Henri. *Science and Hypothesis.* New York: Dover,
Rosnay, Joel de. *Les Origines de la Vie.* Paris: Editions du
Seuil,
Schilder, Paul. *Mind, Perception and Thought.* New York:
Columbia University Press, 1942.
Schrödinger, Erwin. *Mind and Matter.* Cambridge: Cam-
bridge University Press, 1958.
Schrödinger, Erwin. *Science Theory and Man.* New York:
Dover, 1957.
Speransky, A. *A Basis for the Theory of Medicine.* New York:
International Publishers, 1943.
Thompson, D'Arcy. *Growth and Form.* Cambridge: Cambridge
University Press, 1952.
Young, J. Z. *Doubt and Certainty in Science.* London: Oxford
University Press, 1951.
Young, J. Z. *Introduction to the Study of Man.* London: Oxford
University Press, 1971.
Young, J. Z. *The Memory System of the Brain.* Berkeley: Uni-
versity of California Press, 1966.